THE LAND THAT MADE US

THE LAND THAT MADE US

THE PEAK DISTRICT FARMER'S STORY

Edited by Christine Gregory and Sheila Hine
Farming Life Centre

VP First published in 2019 by Vertebrate Publishing.

Vertebrate Publishing. Omega Court, 352 Cemetery Road, Sheffield S11 8FT, United Kingdom.
www.v-publishing.co.uk

Front cover: Simmental cow and calf. Photo: Sheila Hine.
Back cover: From left to right: Carl Turnock making haylage. Photo: Sheila Hine. Haymaking at Sheldon House Farm. Photo: Sheila Hine.
Frank Belfield. Photo: Sheila Hine. Below: Haymaking at Boosley Grange, 1930s. Photo: Courtesy of J. Gilman.
Title page: Traditional damp meadow in May, Leekfrith. Photo: Sheila Hine.

A CIP catalogue record for this book is available from the British Library.

ISBN: 978-1-912560-32-5 (Paperback)

10 9 8 7 6 5 4 3 2 1

Design and production by Ryder Design – *www.ryderdesign.studio*

Published in partnership with the Farming Life Centre and the Peak District National Park Authority, supported by the National Lottery Heritage Fund.

Vertebrate Publishing is committed to printing on paper from sustainable sources.

Printed and bound in Europe by Latitude Press.

THE LAND THAT MADE US

THE PEAK DISTRICT FARMER'S STORY

EDITED BY CHRISTINE GREGORY & SHEILA HINE

Published in partnership with the Farming Life Centre and the Peak District National Park Authority, supported by the National Lottery Heritage Fund.

Vertebrate Publishing, Sheffield.
www.v-publishing.co.uk

Species-rich pasture in the South West Peak. **Photo**: Sheila Hine.

CONTENTS

Quarnford landscape. **Photo**: Sheila Hine.

FOREWORD

Within the lifetimes of many working farmers, agriculture has leap-frogged 400 years – from methods and ways of life that were essentially seventeenth century, into the space age and beyond: remote sensing, genetic engineering, a chemical for every eventuality; all geared to the global market. All this is called 'progress' – and progress is assumed to be all to the good; and if it doesn't always seem that way, we are told that the change has nonetheless been *necessary*. We may take a trip down memory lane, but we cannot re-create the past. It is self-indulgent even to try. But is it really so?

The huge shift into modernity was kick-started by the Atlantic blockade of the Second World War and the sudden, very obvious need to increase home production. The government took over, as Arthur Slack, one of the farmers quoted in this book, recalls: 'The Ministry came round giving lectures and telling you what to do and what not to do.' Land that had never been seriously disturbed – ancient meadows and moorland – was put to the plough, wholesale; cereals planted where none had grown before; stocking rates hugely increased. New technologies came on line: tractors and threshers, artificial fertilisers, DDT. The measures were draconian, but on the whole they worked. Britons were often hungry during and after the war, but there was no mass famine as there might so easily have been. The new technologies brought day-to-day benefits, too.

Says Denise Jarman: 'When my dad bought a baler, it was marvellous, so much easier. My sister and I would walk around the edges of every field and rake in all the last bits.'

A further boost into modern times came in the 1980s when Britain and then the whole world committed itself to the neo-liberal economy: all producers everywhere, including farmers, were obliged to compete in the global market to maximise profits – which, in general, was and is done by maximising output. So the urge to raise production more and more continued in the decades after the war, even when it was no longer necessary. In Europe, modern technology, given a free rein and backed by huge investment, soon produced vast surpluses – 'grain mountains', 'milk lakes' and 'butter mountains' – which the EU tried to curb by imposing quotas and by subsidising whatever was considered to be good. Ever since, free-market economics has co-existed uneasily with the perceived need for governments to intervene and exercise constraint. **>**

The downside is all too obvious. Modern technologies are *designed* to reduce labour in the name of 'efficiency' – meaning cash efficiency. Not only jobs but whole communities and ways of life have disappeared. Hilda Critchlow, like most of this book's contributors, lived way out on the hills, as far from the madding crowds as is possible in the English Midlands, and yet, she says, 'We weren't isolated: there were three farms and three cottages, and everyone was always friendly and you knew everyone up the village … Those days were a lot happier than today. We were busy, but more content.' I have in recent years been earnestly assured by people in positions of influence that hill farmers in particular should be pleased to be put out of work – spared those long cold nights on treeless hillsides playing midwife to ewes. But as Bill Brocklehurst recalls: 'I always loved lambing time. It were like Christmas.' I have never heard farmers complain about the hardship, only about the bureaucracy and the lack of reward.

Wildlife has suffered too, of course. Hundreds of species of wild flowers flourished in the traditional meadows with a host of invertebrates, frogs, voles, and nesting birds (curlews, lapwings, skylarks) – but Britain lost 97 per cent of those meadows between the 1930s and the mid-1990s. Neil Richardson remembers that the black grouse in particular 'were amazing. They were here 365 days, every morning, on their mating arena, the lek site … The black grouse cocks were well proud of themselves and would come and lek every morning and we'd actually get one or two in the garden here feeding on the berries. They were brilliant to see.'

In short: there never was a golden past and we can't re-create what there was, but there's a huge amount to regret nonetheless. Neither can we be content – can we? – with the world's present miseries, from political unrest to mass extinction and climate change – all of which result in part, and sometimes in very large part, from modern industrial agriculture. We need to ask: to what extent has the transformation of farming these past seventy years or so *really* brought net benefit? Clearly, Britain's farming at the start of the Second World War could not provide us with what we needed – but was this because the traditional practices were truly inadequate, or was it because farming between the wars was left to compete with cheap imports, and was otherwise neglected?

Male Green Hairstreak butterfly on hawthorn. Caterpillars feed on a range of plants including bilberry. **Photo**: Christine Gregory.

We should neither seek to resurrect the past and call it 'heritage', nor to assume that all that went before is obsolete. As some academics now emphasise, and some policymakers are beginning to realise, we need instead to treat traditional knowledge with respect – to learn from our ancestors who lived much closer to the realities of nature than we do, and in general had a much better feel for it. Science is vital, of course, but we should use it to build on the wisdom of the past – not, gung-ho, to sweep it aside. More broadly still, we need to re-examine our *values*. What do we really care about? Can a world ruled by the diktats of money and open-mouthed worship of high tech ever be satisfactory? Can it even survive?

All these questions are raised and to some extent answered by this excellent history of modern farming – the best I have come across precisely because the words are those of the farmers themselves and their families, who have lived through and are still living through its transformation. All of them ask, as well we might, where next? •

Colin Tudge
March 2019

Colin Tudge is co-founder of the Oxford Real Farming Conference and the College for Real Farming and Food Culture.

Looking north-west over Wildboarclough to Shutlingsloe. **Photo**: Sheila Hine.

INTRODUCTION

The Land That Made Us is largely composed from around thirty recorded interviews with farmers and land managers from across the south-west area of the Peak District conducted over a period of three years. These accounts cover eighty years of farming history in this remote and rugged landscape. They also reflect a much bigger national story about changing priorities in land use and food production. Generations of farmers give accounts of heroic endeavour in difficult terrain as well as describing day-to-day working and family life. This land had been farmed in traditional ways for centuries. The Second World War changed that, and since then the Common Market (now the EU) and government diktats have constantly rewritten the rulebook for farmers. The next direction of policy and funding priorities in relation to land use, support for farmers and conservation remains uncertain with the outcomes and impacts of Brexit as yet unknown.

In the following accounts, there is pride in achievement as well as frustration at the often conflicting demands of food production and wildlife conservation. This landscape, along with all the productive land on the earth, is now at a crossroads, and what makes for sustainability in the short and the long term is the question central to this book. The Staffordshire Moorlands were once home to the black grouse, and the South West Peak still has nationally important wader populations, but wildlife is under threat here as in the rest of Britain. The future of this landscape, and of the farming communities that help sustain it, hangs in the balance. In this book, it is the farmers' turn to reflect on the past and speculate about the future. **>**

THE SOUTH WEST PEAK – LANDSCAPE AND LAND USE

The South West Peak is a lesser known part of the Peak District, stretching from Lyme Park in the north to Onecote in Staffordshire in the south, and from Macclesfield in the west to Buxton in the east. It falls across three counties: Cheshire, Derbyshire and Staffordshire. Much of it is within the Peak District National Park. Its hills are the outlying south-west uplands and foothills of the Pennines. Its central core is a high moorland plateau covered by blanket peat. The slopes that flank the central uplands are cut through with wooded cloughs that open out to settled pastoral valleys. This is a landscape of contrast. Strongly folded millstone grit gives rise to such dramatic features as the steep slopes and jagged outcrops of the Roaches, Ramshaw Rocks and Shutlingsloe. There is wildness, enclosure, seclusion and drama all within a tract of land bordered by the limestone of the White Peak to the east, the Cheshire and Staffordshire Plains to the west, and the Churnet Valley to the south.

Axe Edge, near Buxton, is one of the principal watersheds of England. The rivers Dove, Manifold and Wye flow south and east to the Humber Basin via the Derwent and Trent, while the Goyt and Dane flow west to the Mersey. This is grazing country, from the central core of unenclosed moorland down through the rough hillside pastures to the lush valleys to the east and the west-facing wooded slopes. On the sheltered margins of the uplands, often tucked into the valleys, are scattered farmsteads, field barns, picturesque villages and tiny hamlets which have been occupied for centuries.

The first farmers here were the Neolithic settlers. Evidence of their homes and crops were discovered in the 1980s in Lismore Fields to the west of Buxton. Several Bronze Age burial mounds remain on the high west-facing slopes of the central moors; and there is an Iron Age hill fort, Castle Naze, above Chapel-en-le-Frith. Archaeological sites, together with ancient drove roads, packhorse routes and trackways, all indicate centuries of human presence and use. Medieval field patterns with small enclosures and open field systems reflect how the uplands were used for grazing and the lower ground for cultivation. Some of the farmsteads dated between the sixteenth and nineteenth centuries may well have medieval origins.

Three medieval hunting forests once dominated the northern part of the area, and restricted settlement in the Middle Ages – Macclesfield Forest in Cheshire, Malbanc Forest in Staffordshire, and part of the Royal Forest of the Peak in Derbyshire. The elite activity of hunting prevailed into the twentieth century, keeping moorland as shoots for the principal landowners in the area.

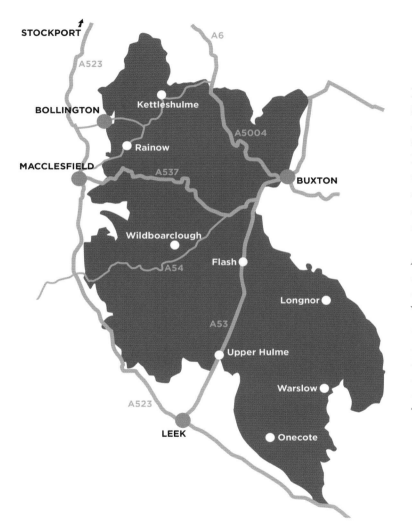

Large tracts of the land were once owned by four major estates: the Swythamley Estate, and the estates of the Harpur Crewe family, the Earls of Derby and the Dukes of Devonshire. The break-up of the Harpur Crewe Estate in the twentieth century is an important part of the farming history of many families featured in this book. There are few clustered estate settlements, and farms tend to be scattered across the landscape rather than being concentrated around the few villages. The dispersed settlement so characteristic of the South West Peak may account for the rugged independence and individuality of those farming in the area today.

Agriculture is dominated by upland livestock farming, and over 95 per cent of the area is grassland or uncultivated. Sheep, beef cattle and some dairying are the principal mainstays, and have been so since the Second World War. Farms range in size from tiny smallholdings of just a few acres through to huge holdings of several hundred acres. What is notable is the high proportion of small farming enterprises. Around half of farms have less than fifty acres (twenty hectares). Farm income tends to be low, especially in the uplands. Almost all of the South West Peak falls within the Agricultural Land Classification (ALC) as poor or very poor.[1] This is, and always has been, farming on the margins. **>**

1 The Agricultural Land Classification is a framework for classifying all farmland in England and Wales according to climate, site and soil – the principal physical factors influencing agricultural production. Land is graded numerically from 1 (excellent) to 5 (very poor). Most of the South West Peak is Grade 4 or 5: poor or very poor quality agricultural land. (MAFF 1988, now Defra.)

The book is mainly organised chronologically. Part 1 covers the war years and the start of government involvement in farming. Part 2 focuses mainly on sheep farming and family life on the area's hill farms from the 1950s to the 1960s. The main focus of Part 3 is on dairying and the trend away from mixed farming as agricultural systems changed and entry into the Common Market led to increased intensification. In Part 4, farmers assess the impact of disease outbreaks – of BSE, foot-and-mouth and the ongoing problem of TB. Some reflect on the increasing pressure to specialise and increase production as milk prices have dropped or stagnated. Part 4 also explores the fundamental shift in direction from production to conservation through grants and subsidies aimed at protecting wildlife, restoring landscapes and emphasising ecosystem services such as carbon sequestration, water supply and flood prevention. South West Peak farmers reflect on this change in priorities, and the gains and losses they have made as a result. In the final part of the book, we hear from incomers, the new generation of local farmers and some of those who know this landscape best as they reflect on the past and assess priorities for the future.

The edited accounts have been transcribed as accurately as possible to convey the energy, rhythms, regional dialect and character of our contributors' spoken words.

THE SOUTH WEST PEAK LANDSCAPE PARTNERSHIP

The book has been funded through the National Lottery Heritage Fund as part of a landscape-wide initiative. Established in 2013, the South West Peak Landscape Partnership is led by the Peak District National Park Authority, working with thirteen other partners, including the Farming Life Centre. The Partnership successfully bid for National Lottery funding through the National Lottery Heritage Fund, and is delivering a programme of work focusing on natural heritage, cultural heritage, farming heritage and communities. The Partnership's mission statement is: 'By working together in the South West Peak, we will shape a better future for our communities, landscape, wildlife and heritage where trust and understanding thrive.' This book attempts to fulfil that aim by raising awareness of the challenges faced by farmers, land managers and conservationists. ●

Christine Gregory and Sheila Hine
July 2019

SOUTH WEST PEAK
LANDSCAPE AT A CROSSROADS

*More information about the South West Peak Landscape Partnership can be found on their website – **www.southwestpeak.co.uk***

The full text of much longer interviews is available to read on the Partnership website.

Fernyford Belted Galloways. **Photo**: Sheila Hine.

Haymaking at Boosley Grange, 1930s. **Photo**: Courtesy of J. Gilman.

PART 1
From horses to tractors
1940s to 1950s

Working with horses; the war years; government involvement in farming; children on the farm; the first tractors and milking machines; power and water come to the hills; the snows of '47.

PART 1: FROM HORSES TO TRACTORS
1940s to 1950s

Mixed farms, in which crops were rotated, and sheep and cattle moved around pastures through the year, were once the bedrock of agriculture across Britain, but the Second World War changed all that. Keeping the country self-sufficient and the population fed became the principal aims of the Ministry of Agriculture and, regardless of topography, soil type or accessibility, the War Agricultural Committees (known as the War Ags) exhorted every farmer and farm worker in Britain to produce more.

The War Ags were first established in 1915 during the First World War and were reinstituted in 1939. They were made up of farmers, landowners and agents, and they had considerable power, controlling the ways that farms were run. After surveying rural land in each county, committees could order work to be done or take possession of farmland. They could decide which crops should be planted where, and they introduced widespread experimental use of pesticides authorised by the Ministry of Agriculture's chief scientist. Between 1939 and the spring of 1940, British farmers increased the total productive land in the UK by 1.7 million acres.

In the South West Peak, the flower meadows and ancient pastures of the low-lying valleys and even the moors and bogs went under the plough if the War Ags made that demand. This was the beginning of an end to hundreds of years of traditional farming in which men, women and children laboured alongside their horses to make what they could of their land.

The transformation of farming began with the war and the advent of the tractor, the coming of electricity and piped water, and increasing mechanisation.

State involvement in farming continued after the war under Clement Attlee's Labour government, in pursuit of reduced food imports and a healthy balance of payments during a time of massive public spending on post-war reconstruction and the new National Health Service.

In 1946, in a drive to use marginal lands for livestock farming, the Hill Farming Act made grants available to improve upland farms. This caused a massive expansion of livestock farming in marginal land. The following year, the 1947 Agriculture Act gave farmers an assured market and guaranteed prices. This set in motion an industrial approach to farming that has altered forever the farming landscapes of Britain. Almost every farmer we spoke to old enough to remember the post-war days recalls the first tractors that changed their working lives. Even the remote hill farms and quiet valleys of the South West Peak felt the winds of change.

Hilda Critchlow lived and worked through this agricultural revolution.

Hilda Critchlow. **Photo**: Christine Gregory.

'I liked working a horse.'

Hilda Critchlow

Hilda was born in 1928 and worked for most of her life on the family's dairy farm, Sheldon House Farm, Brund.

When I left school, I worked with my father. Of course, it was old-fashioned farming in them days with horses. I went to Sheen School, then when I left at fourteen, I helped me father. I had to help my father with the horses, and of course, the war was on.

I remember me father ploughing fields as hadn't been ploughed before. We were ploughing up old hayfields. He'd let me work with one horse by myself, but when there was two horses on a job, he had to be there. We did so much ploughing and drawing rows up; and when there was two horses, I had to be in the middle to hold them, as one went a bit quicker than the other and I had to pull it back. I used to wear high-top shoes and they kept kicking the soil back. Nowadays, you'd say 'I'm not doing it', but you had to do what you were told in them days.

Horse work involved chain harrowing, ploughing and drawing rows up. When it was ploughed, we'd set cabbages or turnips. I liked working a horse. I wasn't afraid of the horses; I was used to them. You'd get a little bit of corn in a bucket and that's how you'd catch them, get a halter on, and bring them home and put them in the stable, give them their water and hay, and get 'em ready for starting work after we'd milked.

There was a brown one that I used to like. He was very quiet. This white one, she was more for going like the devil. She was a bit more dangerous for me, but I never worked her by myself. But the brown one I chain-harrowed with him by myself. If you fetched a horse now and gave me some bridles and gearing, I could do it now: get the collar, turn it round and put it on, then turn it back. You've got to have a knack putting the collar then the gearing on the back.

In wartime, I remember me father with me helping him; he used to work horses 'til they sweat, and he'd have his dinner and wait a while. While they had a rest, he'd listen to the news at one o'clock – see what the war were doing – then go back and fetch the horses.

We had peewits; there was always lots of nests up and down. Same as the cuckoo – you'd always hear the cuckoo. I've never heard that for years and years and years. Same with the peewits. You'd go what they call 'peewit egging'. They wouldn't allow it now – going and getting peewit eggs when we were children. And there was nests up and down various fields. Some fields'd have a lot in them and others would have none. There were curlew and owls.

After the big snows of 1947, the neighbours had a tractor. The year after, me brother had one. I did find I could drive a tractor well, but it weren't like the horse days. My brother sort of took over and I used to do bits of jobs with the horses, but he got doing with the tractor and had no patience with the horses. They hadn't time for the horse. We've got on too quickly going from the horses to the tractor. But the younger ones, they haven't the patience to bother, have they now?

I've been busy all me life, and when me father died in 1976, me brother was left the farm. I've helped him all along life's way until he was taken poorly. We give over milking when I was eighty. I never had a wage. I was keeping house, general work, all to no sense. I ought to have said we'll give over. I was heavy worked, but I could do it.

We weren't isolated: there were three farms and three cottages, and everyone was always friendly and you knew everyone up the village. Now if I go up the village, I have to be taken. I hardly know anyone; it's all different. Those days were a lot happier than today. We were busy, but more content. No one's got time for you now. If there's anything sold, strangers buy them. They might be sociable and they might not. They were happier days – you knew everyone. They were the good old days. Everything were more peaceful. ●

Hilda's brother John Critchlow taking the cows in for milking, 2007. **Photo**: Sheila Hine.

Fred Lownds (Denise Jarman's uncle, see page 64) from Boosley Grange taking milk to Reapsmoor Cheese factory, 1930s. **Photo:** Courtesy of J. Gilman.

Arthur Slack. **Photo:** Christine Gregory.

'Six days shalt thou labour, and on the seventh do odd jobs.'

Arthur Slack

Arthur was born in 1931 at Reddish Farm at Whaley Bridge and worked at Shallcross Farm near Taxal. He died in September 2018.

At home, we were milking by hand; we didn't have a milking machine. We didn't have electric until 1947. We had a big milk round at home. We reared a lot of stock and we had a lot of hens and we had horses. I used to deliver milk with a pony and float.

When I left school in '46, there were four lads at home and obviously we all couldn't stay at home, and I went working on a big farm locally. I started when I were sixteen. This farmer, Mr Lomas, had two sons, one a bit older than me and one younger, and we were milking Ayrshires and we'd tie-ins for seventy-two cows and we milked about seventy-six. That was a big milking herd in those days.

We used to grow a lot of green crops then: cabbages and potatoes and kale and all sorts. It were all labour-intensive. We used to cut leafy kale with a binder and feed it through a chopper into a big wooden silo. That was bloody work, you know. We cut by hand marrow-stem kale with a stem as thick as your wrist, and we grew acres of mangolds at this farm. 'Course, it all had to be harvested by hand; and then in winter, it had to be chopped and mixed with corn. There were always a lot of mowing, muck spreading to do, and you know there were plenty of work. There was always wheelbarrow work; it was all wheelbarrow work in them days.

At Lomas's farm when I went there, there were sixteen horses. I wouldn't say they were all working, but a lot of them were. One of the first jobs I had was burning all this harness, as the role of the working horse was coming to an end. I didn't do any horse farming; I had a tractor, a Standard Fordson.

Mr Lomas was on the War Ag Committee. He used to go every day looking at farms and telling them what they should and shouldn't do. They'd say, 'You've got to plough so many acres.' Well, these people had only got a horse. So the Ministry decided, 'Well, somebody's got to plough this land', so they got these two fellows and they used to go round ploughing. I was tractor-mad at that age – I was about fourteen or fifteen. I were really tractor-mad and I used to come home from school, jump on me bike and I knew roughly where they'd be working. I used to go and help with the ploughing.

It was during the war and just after they wanted everybody to be self-sufficient. The Ministry came round giving lectures and telling you what to do and what not to do, and I went to this lecture at the town hall at Chapel. They were talking about winter milk production then: that's when you want to get the milk, when the price is better and when it's more needed. We were going into this winter milk production getting a calving in August and that sort of thing.

Cos we were retailing milk at home, you had to keep a steady supply of milk. These little Irish cows, if they gave three gallons, you were doing well with them. We had some Irish cattle in the Sheffield blitz. Me dad bought some. They were in wagons in Sheffield three nights in the blitz and when they got them home, you daren't drop a bucket or anything or shut a door. They were gone and they didn't do a lot of good, they didn't; they were shell-shocked.

Anyway, I stopped with Mr Lomas and I enjoyed it; they looked after me. Mrs Lomas was a lady; she looked after me very well and I'd three meals a day, every day. She was wonderful; she just treated me like I was one of her own. I worked half seven 'til about half seven at night. I did six days for Mr Lomas; I never worked on a Sunday. The lads used to say to me at the farm, 'What did you do yesterday?' Cos me dad had a milk round and I went on that on Sunday and they always had this saying: 'Six days shalt thou labour, and on the seventh do odd jobs'. I stopped with Mr Lomas 'til I was twenty and my brother had his fatal accident and I had to come home then.

I look on the toughest bits when I retailed milk with my father. You know in bad winters '63 and '47, you had stockings on your hands; there were no such thing as gloves. It was damn cold, you know. I went to a house one day and come back and said to me father, 'By hell, it's cold in that house.' 'Why? What's up?' 'Well', I said, 'there's mother, father and daughter. They're all sat round with rugs off the floor on them. There's one candle where cold water come into the slops just under the tap to stop it freezing up. No fire.' And he said, 'Get the sledge – let's go back to the farm and get some sticks and coal and logs'. I thought, 'Oh God, Arthur, keep your gob shut; I've made meself a lot of work.' But me dad were like that. He'd never be a millionaire cos he was too kind, yer know. People, a lot of people, were hard up when you delivered milk. ●

'You'd get your head on the side of a cow, milking, and you'd soon be asleep. Oh aye, it was lovely them days. Yeah, but I wouldn't go back to 'em.'

Bill Brocklehurst

Bill was born in 1943. His grandfather was farm bailiff at a farm near Buxton, and later the family had the grazing rights of around 5,300 acres of high moorland around the Cat and Fiddle. Bill, himself a full-time shepherd at the age of fourteen, describes how children were part of the workforce even before they left school.

When me father left school at thirteen, he got a job at Ford Hall at Chapel-en-le-Frith as head horseman. Before he left school, he said at hay time he had to go out, get some horses, rig 'em up, and he had to mow grass. He had t' mow an acre of grass before he went school in morning at hay time. So he were well prepared for dealing with horses and he went to Ford Hall and he were head horseman cos there weren't another horseman. They'd have I don't know how many carthorses for carting their stuff, cos Ford Hall in them days was quite an estate.

Me grandfather, he got the grazing rights on the catchment area for Fernilee Reservoir, but in them days, there were very few sheep. He wanted some help, so me dad moved back up. They lived at Normanwood Farm at Taxal and when he moved back up, they hadn't many sheep and he got a job as rabbit catcher. And he were rabbit catcher all through Goyt Valley and up round Errwood with a gamekeeper from up there. And he caught rabbits all through t' winter, snared 'em and, if it froze 'ard, ferreted 'em. His best tally, he said, one night's snaring were 480 rabbits. They were a big pest and they were a source of income. •

Bill Brocklehurst. **Photo**: Christine Gregory.

'He had t' mow an acre of grass before he went school.'

Harry Gee. **Photo**: Sheila Hine.

Harry Gee

Harry Gee was born in 1923 at The Hayes, Reapsmoor. His family moved to Ridge Farm, Longnor, where he remained for the rest of his life. He died in January 2018.

My dad and Margaret and my brother, they could all milk – of course milking by hand. We hadn't as many cows then as we had later on when the machines come in. When we were mowing, Margaret used to bring me some breakfast down and give horses some grass; they'd settle a bit while they were eating that. I don't know – something nice about it, not like that today.

During the war, everybody had to try and plough a bit. Some people were growing kale and what have you. There were placards up and down, 'Dig for Victory' and all that, you know, and they expected you to plough a bit. There were a lot of land ploughed up during the war and they kept it up for quite a bit after, but as it got seeded down, a lot of it wasn't properly seeded down; it would be seeded down with a short-term ley, not a long-term ley. Well, that werena right thing to do. Some of them didna get touched again, therefore it didn't do as well. It's same now, these silage men – after so many years they're ploughing different areas and reseeding.

The first grants, they come in during the war. Calf subsidy – that was the start of the grant job. At one point, there were quite a bit of grant on draining. We did quite a bit in two or three places. They called it War Ag and they'd sort of draw you a scheme up and tell you what it would cost you when you'd had the grant off it. That's a wet lot, Moorside is. Draining's made it a bit better, but it never gets good compared with some better land.

We started with tractors in 1948 or '49. It helped – the only trouble with these Standard Fordsons, you're alright in the summer time, but in wintertime if you wanted to take the muck out or anything and it were frosty an' icy, eh, they wouldna go. 'Til this four-wheel drive come in, you had to leave it in the muck hole 'til it were dry enough to go. But when four-wheel drive come in, well, it were different ball game altogether. You could get any time with it, get anywhere really.

Horses didn't go straight away; we kept 'em a year or two after that because there were odd jobs we could do wi 'em. We'd got a horse rake – people did raking-up then; they dunna do any now. I can remember using the horse rake and the horse lots and lots of times in these meadows round about here after we had tractors.

We were more or less self-supporting. We'd got milk, and me mother could make butter – she made plenty, no end of butter. You could get a bag of flour; made our own bread. Thursday were baking day. Me mother and our Margaret baked enough bread t' last you a week. We had cheese from down here in Reapsmoor Cheese Factory. ●

'I left school when I were thirteen. All as I wanted to do was get here and work, soft bugger, like I were. Eh dear, if only you could put the clock back.'

Michael Woolley. **Photo**: Christine Gregory.

Michael Woolley
Michael was born in 1941. He was raised on a farm near Hartington.

Dad was renting a farm at Ilam just above Castern Hall – Hilltop Farm, it's called. That's where I was born. I was six month old when we came into Cronkston Lodge, which is between Earl Sterndale and Hartington. It belonged to the Duke of Devonshire. And me dad walked all the cows from Ilam to there [a distance of around nine miles]. They got more land than they'd got cattle to eat it all themselves. They used to take what they call ley stock, you know: people's sheep and people's cows. People hadn't got enough land to keep all the young stock, so they used to take them to ley for the summer. I don't know what it were in them days, but say it were fifty pence a head per week – if you've got fifty, that's twenty-five pounds a week.

We used to grow our own 'taters. No electric, only what we made ourselves. We used to have Tilley lamps for a start; and then when we got engines and used to put a dynamo on with some batteries, we got as we could make twenty-four volts and had twenty-four-volt light. You'd be milking and keep your batteries charged up while you were milking. And the same as if you went out at night, you could switch a light on cos it were twenty-four volt. The battery would put a bulb or two on if you were milking the cows then, and that's how you went on.

I started driving the tractor when I were four. We were tied on. It was the EN27 Ford tractors – them big 'sit up and beg'. I'd be on one side, pushing clutch in; Pete'd be on t' other side putting it in gear. The long shaft came up with your steering arm on, and there were two ropes on. One tied me on one side and he were tied on the other side, so you couldn't fall off. We had to do something; well, we were young. Yeah, you had to be doing something or you'd me dad deal with you. In winter, we had to go and clean his shed out before we went to school; and in summer, we had to go fetch the cows in before we went to school. Everybody was always doing things. Everybody seemed to have their family doing everything. You know they were all involved in it; you just accepted it and got on with it. If you didn't do what you were told, you got your ears boxed. ●

Frank Belfield. **Photo**: Sheila Hine.

'You had t' get out and do something, not like they do nowadays.'

'That was a big lift, like – see a cow being milked while you could stand and watch it when you'd been used to sitting under it.'

Frank Belfield

Frank was born in 1942 at Brownsett Farm, Meerbrook, where he still lives.

Me Granny and Granddad Belfield on me mother's side came here in 1904. They'd a biggish family, so they'd plenty of home-reared help. They didn't farm very intensively. It were all horse work in them days. It'd be about 140 acre then, rented from Swythamley Estate. They had a bit of help in and they built it up and got it going. In them days, when any of the young 'uns wanted to leave home, they rented 'em somewhere. You couldna go buy owt. As each one left home, they took a portion of stock and rented a farm. Think three of them went on to [Lord] Derby's Estate round the Clough [Wildboarclough] and they carried on 'til there were only me mother left. Then me dad come here, and then they started on their way, like, and I'm still here. Mother was born here, I were born here, and I'm on borrowed time. I've done me three score years and ten and a bit, and I've seen an awful lot o' changes in it. I can remember working the horses. We did have a tractor – an owd Standard Fordson – but I've come from working the horses to a bit more modern way o' doing things. I remember the milking machine coming in 1947. That was a big lift, like – see a cow being milked while you could stand and watch it when you'd been used to sitting under it.

We had dairy cattle, but you reared all your own replacements. Any surplus was sold on either for beef or whatever. And they'd have sheep above the road where it were worse doing, because we didn't keep cattle up there 'til hill cow subsidy started. That was when we started putting Angus and hill type cows up there, and me dad didn't overstock.

At the end of the war when food was still on ration, the lambs were graded. They took 'em to market and the Ministry took them and they were weighed. One of the butchers and a farmer representative judged whether they were up to standard or not. One for the farmer, one for the butchers; then they went off to slaughterhouse. They were issued back to the local butchers. They had their quota cos there weren't enough to go round. They could only have what they could let 'em have. And then of course free-market trading developed after, soon as rationing finished. Of course, folks started wanting to keep more stock and there got a bit more mechanisation. Before, it were all pitchfork to get the hay with and horse-drawn tackle to work it, and then tractors started coming in, and soon baling come in. ●

THE SNOWS OF '47

The snows of 1947 have become the stuff of legend. During this long
hard winter, there had been two earlier periods of cold weather, in
December 1946 and early in January 1947, but the severest weather
began on 21st January and persisted through to mid-March 1947 with
immense snowfall and persistent freezing easterly winds locked over
Britain by an anticyclone across Scandinavia. The whole of Britain was
affected through this harshest of winters with coal and food shortages,
and the near-total disruption of industry, transport and farming.
Herds of animals froze or starved to death, and sheep farmers
across Britain lost one quarter of their flocks.

A snow clearing team in the South West Peak, 1947.
Photo: Courtesy of Dave and Doreen Graham and the Friday Club.

Michael Woolley

I was born in 1941, so I'd be six, but I can remember '47 snow, no problem. Well, everybody seems to remember that, don't they? And people now say, 'Blimmin eck, in't there some snow!' I says, 'Snow? You've seen nothing yet. Why,' I says, 'when you've seen the telegraph poles sticking out through top like that,' I says, 'that's snow.' Cos in '47, you couldn't get milk out for about three or four months. We were snowed in. We got fifty-something pigs and run out of corn, but we'd got plenty o' hay and straw. They used to chuck 'em some hay and straw and tip milk to 'em. Every time they heard a bucket rattle, they used to be squealing, but it kept 'em alive. It were milk – nothing else we could do with it. Me mother used to go round and skim all the cream off the top and make butter. There were stacks of butter she used to make. ●

'When you've seen the telegraph poles sticking out through top ... that's snow.'

Harry Gee

'47 snow, bloomin' heck, I shall never forget that! Rationing were still on then. In '47, there were nothing going off, nowt went past here, that big snow. There were no snow blowers and big shovels out of the quarry then. There werena any, just men. Quarries could do nowt, there were too much snow about; and of course, the men out of the quarries were on the roads with shovels. Council paid the men to clear the roads.

We were alright because we'd got pretty well o' fodder. There were some of these places higher up they'd got nowt. They kept managing and managing. During the snow, there'd be three or four gangs of men between Warslow and Longnor; and Tom Sutton, he were gangmaster. He were setting 'em all on and seeing as they'd all got shovels and everything. Well, during the night, the wind'd get up and blow it in again, and it would be so much higher the next day for t' throw it out, and this went on for quite a bit. I can remember one wagon coming up past here with a load o' fodder on; it were rough: I mean it had only been shovelled out as best they could. He were rocking about; he did manage to get through eventually. I think it were summat do with NFU [National Farmers' Union]. It went to Hardingsbooth and people fetched it from there with horse and cart, or horse and sledge – anything.

Derek Buxton with horse sledge at the top of Onecote, 1947. **Photo**: Bill Ratcliffe (deceased).

Bill Brocklehurst

When it were big snow coming, most of these old moorland ewes knew. They'd clear off from an area and go somewhere where they felt they were safer. Except in 1947 and your '63 winter where it was so severe and being so big amounts of snow, it swamped 'em … nowhere to go; they couldn't get anywhere. ●

'It were so severe … it swamped 'em.'

Water froze up; you had to take care of it. This were the only water we had. This spring never went dry, but we kept it covered up. My dad got some galvanised sheets, or perhaps a section off a collapsed hen cote or something, and some old carpet – anything to keep the wind out and the frost out – and that's how we managed. To water the cows, we had to uncover it while they come out and had a drink. ●

Swaledale sheep in snow. **Photo**: Christine Gregory.

PART 2
Last of the old days and ways
1960s to 1970s

A shepherd's life; the value of wool; farming subsidies; sheep dipping; local sheep sales; family life on a remote hill farm.

PART 2: LAST OF THE OLD DAYS AND WAYS
1960s to 1970s

Sheep farming has shaped much of the landscape that we know today, with woodland clearance, early enclosure, grazing of uplands and draining of marshland. During the Middle Ages, the export of English wool was the chief source of the country's wealth and the Church's economic power. Then, upland moors, bog and marsh, unfit for cultivation, were suitable only for sheep grazing, and the value of wool was such that packhorses would have carried it over long distances from remote areas across the Peak District. From the 1930s, an increased polarisation of farming in Britain meant that arable farming was concentrated in the drier and warmer south and east of Britain, while sheep and cattle farming became more concentrated in the cooler, wetter north and west. The expansion of upland livestock farming, begun in the post-war period, increased massively after Britain joined the Common Market in 1973. European funding for hill farmers was based on the number of stock through what are called headage payments. Sheep numbers in the uplands of the Peak District almost tripled in just forty years, increasing from an average of 16,483 sheep on 58,586 acres (23,709 hectares) in the early 1930s to 48,966 by the mid-1970s.

Sheep farming has a long history in the remote and rugged uplands of the South West Peak, but until more recent times, most farming families in the uplands also kept milk cows, beef cattle, poultry and pigs. The hardship, endurance and skills of hill farmers reflect an ancient way of life, and sheep farming is central to the farming culture and identity of the area. It is hard to believe how recently water was drawn from wells, light came from Tilley lamps and farmers generated their own electricity. There is a timeless quality to these accounts of shepherding and subsistence farming from a forgotten age in which small children might search for buried sheep at night equipped only with candles in jam jars; a time when teenagers became farmers in their own right and when every member of the family had a role to play.

Bill Brocklehurst

Bill Brocklehurst knows the moors of the South West Peak in ways that few people can ever know a landscape. Bill became Peak District National Park warden on the Roaches in 1999 and retired in 2013; but for most of his life, he was first and foremost a shepherd.

'I was a shepherd for a pound a week and me keep.'

I left school at fifteen and me dad bought me a good working dog and a pair of horsehide boots built on a full-sprung last. The toes turn up on 'em. He bought them from a firm at Rothbury called Rogersons and they specialised in making hill boots for gamekeepers and hill shepherds. They were made out of horsehide and a pair'd last me two years. And he said, 'Get a saw and go down and cut yourself a stick.' So I was a shepherd then for a

Bill Brocklehurst the shepherd as a boy in 1952. **Photo**: Family photograph taken by a passing hiker.

pound a week and me keep. I worked for me dad; there were no thought of getting a job or doing anything else. The labour was needed at home. Me brother who was five years older was already working on t' farm, and me sister got married and went just as I were leaving school. In them days, I think dad 'ad only an odd cow just for our own use, and everything were just geared round sheep.

I was born '43. Me granddad started off. He were a farm bailiff at a farm just outside Buxton. Then when the opportunity came for t' get this farm at Oldfield, and this big area of land for running sheep on, he took it. I think we had about 5,300 acres, a huge area. There were nobody else on it at this time; and then, as the years went on, one of me uncles came in with me granddad and one or two people round top boundaries – they ran a few sheep on. There'd probably only be four or five men. It was all walking. If you started rounding your sheep up at Cat and Fiddle, you walked up there first. It were four mile or more. It was all I knew, it was all I knew.

HEFTED FLOCKS

If you can get like a proper moorland breed, they would be hefted – hefted flocks. Now there's nobody would go and heft 'em, and it's dying out. A hefted lamb is born on an area of moorland and it's reared there, and if you took it ten mile away, it'd always go back to same spot where it were born and sorta reared. It's a thing that's instilled in your hill breeds – the Swales, Herdwicks, your Rough Fells; and round 'ere in them days,

Bill with two of his champion Gritstones in 1988. **Photo**: Monica Brocklehurst (Bill's wife).

it were all Derbyshire Gritstones and Woodlands. It's their natural instinct. It'll keep going back through the generations, and one ewe lamb, when it's lambed, its lamb will heft to that area, so long as you don't take 'em away or sell 'em. Leave 'em out and it's self-motivated. Its heft, it might be fifty acres, might be ten acres, what sheep'd live on, but it'd know. It's mother'd teach it where for t' go in twelve months as to what were growing and what were eatable and what would do. It were very rare you got a poorly one. If they did get poorly, alright they'd die and foxes'd eat 'em – you know, end of messing.

I've been in sheep all me life. When I were showing Gritstones in about 1988, I won the male and female champion at Royal Show with Gritstones. I won Champion Gritstone at Royal Welsh Show for three years in late '80s, early '90s. Now I've got a big carrier bag full of rosettes from me dad. He showed sheep all his life. Wherever Royal Show were in those days (cos it moved around), him and a few other farmers in t' area, they'd troop off and be there for t' week. Me dad kept Derbyshire Gritstones always. They were lovely sheep; they're very versatile, hardy, got a good long carcass, a good fleece. Most of Gritstone wool went for hosiery.

'Wool's worth nothing now.'

When I were still in t' school, I used for t' go round shows with me dad, and we just showed wool. At Todmorden Show up at Lancashire, me dad always went there showing. I think I were unbeaten for donkey's years in t' wool class. They always showed it on t' hoof, still on t' sheep. Then in latter years, we started showing fleeces, cos they did away wit' on t' hoof fleece classes. So we had t' take actual fleeces, and we had some very nice trophies what I've won from them. Your Swaledales, it's all t' carpet and mattress packin'. Herdwick – that's a bit coarse. When we were younger, Patons and Baldwins took all our wool. I think you can still buy knitting wool made be them; 'course then they got swallowed up by British Wool Marketing Board. But every time wool went in, me dad always loaded us lads up and we went up and saw it graded, and had a big hot dinner off 'em and it was very eye-opening. So we selected our rams not only for meat quality, but for wool quality. Cos in them days, your fleece was quite a worthwhile project. Wool's worth nothing now.

'In them days, we were shepherds.'

In them days, we were shepherds. There were no four-wheel-drive motorbikes. You walked, you walked everywhere; and when you were walking, you were seeing things.

When I were young, you didn't get worms in moorland sheep, cos they were so thin on that they didn't get a worm buried in 'em. If they got maggots, if they got blown, you found 'em in time, so you'd know. If you were out and walking, you saw all these things. 'Course, if they got blown, they tended for t' go in bracken beds out of sight, and if you didn't see 'em, you always had a good dog and dog'd wind 'em, so you'd go with your dog – he'd find 'em.

Before lambing, like, obviously you'd round up, and some of t' sheep we lambed outside because we hadn't enough in-bye land for t' bring 'em in for t' lambing; and a fair lot, you know, they were lambed out in t' open. And you needed a good dog at lambing time. I always loved lambing time. It were like Christmas. And then, you know, when that'd finished, you'd have to set to and round 'em all up and ear-mark 'em. All lambs were ear-marked then, no tags or anything. Ear-marking was a series of notches in your lamb's ear. When they were notched, that were with 'em 'til they died. These agricultural merchants as made all these things for agriculture, they made all these different shapes. I've still got me ear-markers. I've still got them. All these different farms, they all had a specific either raddle mark or ear mark.

'Forgot t' tell farmers … "it'll kill you".'

Usually July, you'd start on shearing. Odd years, we'd shear; and then the next morning, you'd find one or two had frozen t' death, it was that cold. When you sheared, you brought 'em in, sheared 'em, dipped 'em in plenty of arsenic dip for t' kill bugs on 'em, mark 'em ready for t' let 'em out again next day. Next day, you'd gather next piece of land in. The dip were in liquid form from when I first remember, but my dad said when they first started, it come in like a block of soap, and that were arsenic. So they had to cut it up, melt it in hot water for put it in t' dip. The big thing in them days was sheep scab. It'd decimated a lot of sheep flocks, so government brought in that all sheep had got t' be dipped and immersed. Cooper, McDougall and Robertson made a lot of sheep dip in those days. And to start off, it come like a block of soap, and then they perfected it into a liquid. I never heard tell of anybody dying from using that. Then there was dieldrin dip, organochlorine that were killing eagles or something if they had dead sheep. As they went on, they got onto this organophosphorus stuff. Forgot t' tell farmers, you know – 'be careful, it'll kill you'.

There was no training; only person that came out was policeman. You had to inform police you were dipping in those days; they had to come out and get their watch out, see as that sheep'd been in t' tub for a minute. Some of t' policeman come out and time every sheep 'til they got fed up and went; but others'd come out and look at dip tub, have a cup of tea and bacon butty. ●

George Brocklehurst (Bill's father) with his prize-winning Gritstone ram at Normanwood Farm, Taxal, 1940s. **Photo**: Walter Sidebottom (deceased)

ABOUT SHEEP DIPPING

Sheep are affected by several parasites inhabiting the fleece, the skin and, in some cases, the flesh of the living animal. They have no natural protection against these pests, which can cause considerable suffering, loss of condition and death. Sheep's oily fleece make the penetration of treatments difficult, and so the chemicals used are extremely potent. The dipping process involves the sheep's total immersion, bringing those involved into extensive contact with hazardous substances. The arsenical dips that Bill refers to were in use from the early nineteenth century and were still approved for use into the mid-twentieth century.

Sheep scab is a notifiable disease spread by mites, and entire flocks were compulsorily dipped to halt the spread of it. In the 1940s, sheep were being treated with organochlorine insecticides. Scab was eradicated in Britain in 1952, but a further outbreak in 1972 led to compulsory dipping in the 1970s, with the notoriously dangerous DDT or dieldrin (an organochlorine pesticide developed to replace DDT). These highly toxic chemicals (also used in seed dressings) leached off the land and into the river systems, and sometimes excess chemicals were simply emptied onto the ground or into watercourses. By the mid-1970s, otters had disappeared from most of England as a result of high concentrations of toxins in their body tissue caused by a process called bioaccumulation. Chemical residues in invertebrates moved through the food chain to fish, then the otter – the top predator. Aerial predators including the peregrine and sparrow hawk were similarly affected. In time, the damaging effects of organochlorine insecticides on wildlife – and also the potential effects

on human health – were understood, and dieldrin was gradually withdrawn from use until it was finally banned in 1989.

The next generation of agricultural pesticides were the organophosphates (OPs) that Bill refers to, and the effects of which are described by Rob Belfield on page 52. Prolonged and repeated exposure to OPs has led to numerous cases of severe neurological problems, including multiple sclerosis, memory loss, fatigue and depression. In some cases, this has led to suicide. The number of farmers who have suffered ill health through dipping sheep is currently unknown, but some estimate it could run into thousands.

The next chemical fix was synthetic pyrethroid insecticides which, while less dangerous to mammals (including humans), proved devastating to aquatic invertebrates. According to Buglife, an organisation devoted to the conservation of invertebrates, 'Synthetic pyrethroids are 1000 times more toxic to wildlife than previously used chemicals. A few drops of Cypermethrin dripping from a wet sheep into a stream will kill all the invertebrates for up to ten kilometres downstream, with knock-on impacts for fish, the rest of the aquatic ecosystem and fishing businesses.'

Following a Buglife campaign, in 2006 the Veterinary Medicines Directorate suspended the licence to sell the synthetic pyrethroid Cypermethrin for sheep dipping on environmental grounds, and in 2010 Cypermethrin was permanently withdrawn from sale in the UK.

The specific problem of sheep dips reflects a much wider problem of pesticides in the environment at a time when a collapse in insect numbers has been detected across Europe.

At the end of the dipping, Bill describes what happened to the dip: 'Plug were knocked out of bottom of t' dip and percolated in them days … it percolated.'

Bill Brocklehurst

When I left school, we walked 'em to Buxton Market, sheep what we were selling, and it were my job with a dog on a piece of string to walk in front so that sheep couldn't get too far ahead like. The cattle market at Buxton, it's a car park now. They were in hurdles. We walked them from halfway up Long Hill. Probably walk 'em about four mile. We'd go cross-country part way, then follow t' main road. You didn't see many cars, though. We had t' walk 'em back down Terrace Road and put 'em in cattle pens at Buxton Station. There were a guy from Northamptonshire used to come and buy draft ewes. He'd have trucks ordered down off British Rail and they'd go by rail down to Northampton. Draft ewes were sheep had done about three years on t' hill – they'd be starting wearing out a bit by then, and anything as me dad didn't like, some as'd be buggers for straying, also surplus lambs and a few breeding tups, he'd take them.

'We walked 'em to Buxton Market.'

Dad'd only buy tups. Sheep sales were mainly round September going into October. They used to for t' go t' Haslingden Market in Lancashire – there were a big sheep sale there. He'd be able t' buy Gritstone tups there, keep buying fresh blood. All t' ewes were Gritstone, home-bred females. Once they'd got a flock established, they never bought any females. Sales'd be once a fortnight, and last sale right at end of October, and very often it'd be snowing at Buxton.

The tups would go out with ewes about 21st November. We brought all t' sheep in t' land, and it were sorting 'em out as'd been reddled, to take t' pressure off land. We had Venetian red powder and engine oil, mixed it up in a tub. We had a flat stick and one lad caught tup, sat him up; other one went up and rubbed some of this on his brisket; then next tup they reddled. So when they mounted sheep, they left a red mark and we'd have t' sort 'em. Anything with a red rump, that went in one pen and they went back out on t' moor. All others went in t' other pen and back in t' field. We used to reddle about every couple of days. Most of 'em'd be tupped within three weeks. We hadn't enough grass for t' feed 'em all. The marked ones went through t' yard gate; we just tipped 'em out and next day, they'd be back at Cat and Fiddle – they'd all be back on their own territory. That would take us into winter, into December; and then when it snowed, there were fox catching.

Ewes with Texel cross lambs. **Photo**: Sheila Hine.

We used to have horrendous problems with foxes when we were lambing out. If there were a bit of snow, you saw where they were, and I sent for gamekeeper and he popped a terrier in t' hole and when it came out, he shot him. That went on all through t' winter. In them days, you'd 'appen have twenty or thirty. But me best year, and that'd be early '70s, I had 120 adult foxes and twenty-two litters of young 'uns. And don't forget, Lord Derby had two or three full-time gamekeepers at top end of valley and on Axe Edge moors, and they were at 'em all t' time. Combs Moss had a full-time gamekeeper on. We dug 'em out. Most of the cubs were born in April. If you didn't get the adult foxes, you couldn't leave any cubs because they'd be gone within that night. You hadn't stopped your lamb-killing. And, you know, these people stand up on t' telly and say, 'Oh, foxes won't kill a lamb.' They bloody well do. Oh yes, I've seen it happen. You'd get a sheep down if you were having a difficult lambing, and if it couldn't get up the next morning, they'd rip its ear off. They love sheep's ears for some reason. Don't know why, what were tasty about them? Foxes with cubs, they were terrible killers for us. If they hadn't got cubs, they might have an odd lamb; they weren't as much trouble at all.

Carrion crows, they were horrendous. We'd full battle against them. If your sheep went down for t' lamb, they'd creep up on it on blindside and whip its eye out. If lamb weren't fully out … tongue and eyes out. This weren't just odd occasions, it were regular. We once had trouble with a gull killing lambs, pecking 'em on top of head. Newborn lambs, you know, a day or two old, they spend most of their time asleep. We started finding these lambs with two or three holes pecked on their head. We didn't know what it were. And me dad went on top of hill with binoculars one day whilst we were lambing and just sat there, and he saw this great big gull. I think they were black-backed or something. This great big gull walked up and pecked its head. So then we watched for them coming and they got a lead injection.

'Foxes with cubs, they were terrible killers for us.'

If you 'ad a sheep as'd lost a lamb or something had killed lamb, you took it home. You'd either get a twin lamb or an orphaned lamb. You'd get that lamb and put skin on the new one and foster it out. So you were doing that, like at night-time, when you got round to it. We always had cade lambs and if you'd got a lot left at end of t' season – if they were doing alright, you'd carry on feeding 'em. Oh yes, we had pets. When I were little, I didn't have playmates; I only had cade lambs. ●

'When I were little, I didn't have playmates; I only had cade lambs.'

Swaledale sheep gathered. **Photo**: Christine Gregory.

Rob Belfield

Born to a farming family in the 1960s, Rob farms at Hurdlow Farm. Like so many farmers in the marginal lands of the South West Peak, his farm alone couldn't support a family. The main income came from the family haulage business.

We had a lot of sheep; those days it was all Gritstones, Rough Fells – hill sheep. Me granddad was very good at building sheds, but he wasn't much of a stockman; he just thought, keep lots of them and things will work out alright. He'd have 500 in those days, or more, because it was open grazing. The hills round at the top didn't have any fences. When they had twigged to fence everything in, they realised they could cram them in. In the early days, when he had got 100, he was the talk of the town; but there was no fences, so they would fetch them back from The Winking Man most days, cos they'd just turn out and they'd set off. Nobody did bother; they were all marked up in them days, and they just went and fetched them. 'Til they could get the Strines and the Mermaid fenced properly, they sort of disappeared. We always had a red mark on the left hip. Wains next door was on the right hip and on the shoulder. Eric Williams was a horseshoe. So we all knew who everybody's was. They all got mixed up, but everyone seemed to just take it, as everybody did the same.

'Hill farming has never ever paid.'

The first sheep I had were some Cluns. Me granddad fetched them from Church Stretton. I was obsessed with sheep farming. I wasn't really much into the cows at that stage. They packed up milking before I was born, then they decided to have suckler cows. Back in them days, with big numbers we were paid a big subsidy. The headage payment was on the animals, so if you had one sheep having one lamb, that was good enough. It was a way of increasing production but still keeping it cheap food for the consumer.

Subsidies have ruled my life one way or another, and even with subsidies, they had the wood shavings business because the farming didn't really make enough. If you want to expand and grow, you have got to do something else, so it's never actually paid in the true sense of a business. Hill farming has never ever paid; I can't see how it does, how it ever has or how it ever will without some financial support.

After the war, they got these ideas of production subsidies. My granddad thought, 'Get some fences up, keep as many sheep as we can, milk that as much as we can.' The environment didn't really matter much in those days, though we didn't use any fertiliser, any spray or anything. In those days, it was cheaper to spread your muck, keep lots of animals to keep the weeds down. We used to go round with scythes all summer scything thistles. That was a waste of time cos they just grew again, but that is what we did.

I always had me own sheep. They always wanted me to join in with rugby at school. I never would cos it was sheep sale day. Saturdays were not for messing about kicking a ball; I was gone to sheep sales with me granddad, or me and Arthur. When I got driving, as soon as I could, we were off and we used to go to Haslingden buying sheep. We used to go to Clitheroe, Bakewell and Leek and Hartington.

'They'd take the sales to the sheep … it was something that kids now will never see.'

We used to have the sales in the fields and it was such a big tradition every autumn. There was the two or three sales at Hartington, and there's the field at Biggin. They got up to 20,000 on one day. I mean it was a spectacle, really. So we were breeding store lambs purposely to go to these sales. Don't ask me how many sheep there were in the country then – there must have been a lot. We did Hartington. There was Bury and Hilton. They had the sales at Hulme End. They tried one at Meerbrook. There was one at Morridge, Wildboarclough – that was a good one. That was Bagshaws, and they did one at a place called Chunal on edge of Glossop. The cattle markets weren't big enough, so they'd take the sales to the sheep. But it was something that kids now will never see. We always used to go, sell our lambs, go and have a drink cos there'd be a pub nearby, near to the sheep sale. Granddad always bought us dinner and that. You know, it was just exciting to go. So I always thought it was very, very sad when they stopped. It had to go. It would be a logistical nightmare if they tried it again now, but it was tradition.

There was a lot more of us then, the amount of sheep farmers. Everybody had a few. They'd have the Hartington sale generally for the Hartington people, and Morridge for the Morridge people, but then we did take them everywhere, and if we had a bad do we had to load them up and bring them back. It would be like nine and ten o'clock at night, finding 'em and bringing 'em back.

There was the compulsory dipping. If you took them to Hartington, the big sales, if they weren't dipped, they would just turn away from them. They didn't want 'em. You had to state that they had been dipped, so it was something we had always done. Ever since I could walk, I had been dipping sheep. Then me and Ruth put in a big circular bath up the top of the yard, which was a big idea then. You could get eight sheep in it at a time. Ruth stood in the middle with a plunger and I used to chuck them in. That was the OP [organophosphate] dips. I have definitely got OP poisoning because I have been doing it all my life. They say you have to wear masks, you have to wear gloves. Twenty-five degrees middle of August chucking eight sheep middle of summer, you don't wear anything you don't need to. I am contaminated. I used to get a bit of a cold after dipping. You get wet jeans. Later on, I would get big spots on my legs like proper zits, but I never really put two and two together cos people didn't. It was just after dipping.

One night I do remember. I am one of the most placid people you could ever come across. We went to a Young Farmers do at Trentham and I was that ill-tempered, I could have fallen out with anybody. I could have thumped anyone and Ruth said, 'What is up with you, what is up with you?' And I couldn't understand it. We came home. I didn't hit anyone, didn't get in trouble, but I was just foul-tempered. Anyhow, it happened again next year, and we put it down to the dip and it was changing me personality somehow. We were on the OP dips then. The pyrethroids

were better for the sheep and supposedly for us, but worse for the watercourses, weren't they? It was compulsory dipping; we'd got to do it. The police came and watched you do it to make sure you dunked them for a minute. It did the sheep good, but it didn't do us any good. It never affected Ruth. She was in the thick of it. She never understood why it affected me, but one night I went to bed and I started shaking and shivering and I couldn't stop. My legs were uncontrollable, shaking, and I said, 'Never again am I using that.' So we didn't. We never used the dip hole again. We went on to Spot On. We went two or three years with nothing; we used Dectomax if ever we have any scab. We haven't seen any scab for ten years anyway. We use Click for maggots, Ectofly if any of 'em start itching, but we are not ever, ever dipping sheep again cos I think it would get me again. ●

Kath Belfield. **Photo**: Sheila Hine.

Kath Belfield

Kath was born in 1958 and now lives on a smallholding near Leek. Over the years, she has worked in factories, as a coffin maker, and at a slaughterhouse and knacker's yard. She even ran her own kennel business, but farming remained her passion and she was born to it.

I was born at Strines Farm, Upper Hulme near Leek, a little remote place just below Mermaid. I was second to youngest out of ten. I had great parents. Me mam and dad, Arthur and Alice, were reyt good folk, hardworking, good character. Dad was known as 'Taffy Jack of all trades'. His dad died when he was ten, so they had to pull him out of school. When he was thirteen, he had to run the farm. All the responsibilities laid on him. The farm was rented, part of the Crewe and Harpur Estate. Me dad had polio when he was seventeen and he come out of hospital and for t' get going (cos he couldn't walk up hill), for t' get his legs going, he had to walk back'ards up hills. First he had to sit down back'ards, then he got going by walking back'ards on sticks. That's what got him going again. Then he had a motorbike, cos he could ride a motorbike, you see. Then he learned how to drive a car with moving his legs with his hands, and then he ended up taxiing. He used to sort of run (it wouldn't be an official jobbie then) a taxi up in the hills. And that is where he met me mother, running folk to dances on a Friday and Saturday night. Me mum was born in 1916. Me dad was older. I think me dad was born in 1908.

Me mum was a good milker, me mother was. Me dad couldn't milk with being crippled. He couldna join army for national service, but he ended up with a threshing box. So it tended to be me dad out with threshing box all winter, and me mum did all the milking.[2] We were all born in the middle bedroom and she had never been in hospital until she was eighty-two. She had ten kids, me mother. She milked in the morning, had me at eleven o'clock and she milked again at night. Folks say you've got it hard today, but they dunna know they are born, really.

The day after I was born, there come a blizzard. I was born on 17th April 1958, and they were all out fetching sheep and lambs in cos they'd been lambing, and they said they had sheep and lambs everywhere out of snow to save them. They said the house was full, full of boxes. The day after, at about nine o'clock at night, the lads were out with candles in jam jars looking for sheep, you know, best they could. And the lads wouldna be great ages, would they? Our Ann come in and did a great ruck of snappin' and she said, 'That kid's never been fed.' They reckon I had nowt to eat since eight o'clock in morning, never woke up, never skriked nor nothing. But they said house was full of lambs and sheep. They said it was chaos. They even got 'em up upstairs.

Me mother was always very proud she had ten kids and reared ten, cos not many did that. There was a lot of losses and there were a lot of folk couldn't afford to feed their kids. They had to farm them out – like all our

'She had ten kids, me mother. She milked in the morning, had me at eleven o'clock and she milked again at night.'

2 The threshing box that Kath refers to was a piece of farm equipment that threshed corn to separate the grain from the husks and stalks. The machines were powered initially by steam engine, then by tractor, and were a forerunner to the combine harvester.

lads as they grew up. Once they left school, they went and worked away from home and lived in. Me mam and dad went round and picked the places for 'em to go. In a way, they were farmed out to make space for us little ones. It was three bedrooms: mam and dad in middle bedroom, girls at far end with one bed, and lads had first bedroom with stairs going up and just a wardrobe to separate. When our Ann was courting Geoff, Geoff used to stop and sleep with lads, bunk in. But cos I was one of little 'uns, I was lucky really as I had two big 'uns on either side me. I was always snug – you know what I mean? I never had a cot – we all started life in a drawer; then you went from drawer to between two chairs; and when you could get out of that, you were big enough for bed. That's how we did us all. Happy days. They were good parents, good folk, really.

We were always happy. There was always summat going on. We were always busy, but it's good busy when you are a kid, in't it – stuff happening. The lads go off working, all come for Sunday dinner with their wages. Me mam had wages off them all, then give them pocket money. When you were eighteen, you give board and lodgings. When I was sixteen, I give me mum a wage and she'd give me pocket money. Then when I was eighteen, I paid board and lodgings and was responsible for my own money.

The milk went in churns in the old van. I suppose when others were younger, it'd be horse and cart, but me father had a van. It went to top of Podmores drive, top of Cat Tor. Everybody round that area left it there. There was a big stand at top of Cat Tor and everybody took it up to the stand, like. If there was any messages or anything like that, folk used put notes under return churns. You'd leave your message and churn man used to check. He was a bit like postman, really.

Dad'd had polio, but other than t' milking he could do every job. He always said there's always two ways of looking at everything. If you can't do something one way, if you think about it, there's always another way. I think that, in general, most farmers are good at that. They're a breed that'll always work things out.

At shearing, they would drive three stakes in and tie him up to them. Us little 'uns would wind the fleeces and big 'uns took sheep to him. He taught all lads to shear. He learned 'em all on dead sheep. They started 'em very young, but they all sheared dead sheep for to start with – any that died. They did that with hand clippers. Wool was worth more than the sheep then, so all lads learned to shear very young.

In 1947, me dad was in hospital. He was servicing the threshing box. It dragged him and he went through threshing box. He come out knocked to bits. All he had left on was his collars and cuffs and rim off the top off his welly. It had knocked him to bits and he were eight week in hospital. He come out and got over that. When he'd had polio at seventeen, they told him he wouldn't have kids, so he had ten to prove them wrong. Marvellous fella, me dad. He had the patience of Job. If he was learning you how to tie your shoelaces, it didn't matter if you had thirty goes, he'd keep showing you. He showed me loads of stuff. He even showed me how to sharpen a penknife. It didn't matter how long it took you learn it; he had patience of Job. Happen that's with his suffering.

When me mum and dad were up at Strines, me dad had bought his first Jersey cow, come from Jersey. He had been to pick that up from Liverpool Docks, seen it swing over in a cargo net. He went to fetch her. They called her Merrivale. For three months after she calved, me mum milked her three times a day. She give twelve gallon a day in the '50s. Anyone could come and watch. She didn't need to tell lies, the cow spoke for herself, anyone could see. There was none as good as her; they said she was a star turn, and she wore for years and years and years. It was a lot at the time.

Me dad died when I was eighteen, which impacted greatly on me, which it does when you're young. I made me dad's coffin, fully lined it. Very proud of that, lovely job.

Me mother said, 'We're not having you farming.' Me mum and dad were dead against it; they didn't want us having a mauling life like they had had – a mauling life. She said, 'Edie's got you a job in Halle Models factory. You start there Monday.' I was an apprentice sewer. I was very, very bad at it.

Despite the warnings from her mum, Kath got work on a farm.

I went working for Frank Barber at Little Tidnock Farm, Gawsworth. We were milking, sheep, a bit of arable – grew a bit of barley, learned how to plough. We'd never had tractors or owt like that. I learned a lot. Frank gave me basis for more modern farming. Frank carried on farming exactly as his father had. Frank's father was a very progressive farmer – he was first farmer to have a tractor and first man to have a baler, but Frank kept everything the way his dad had done it. He'd sell his calves, but if owt had got or had shits or a gimpy leg or summat, he'd keep it. It'd do for the bull, so a lot of cows left a bit to be desired. They were a bit of all sorts and Frank was happy with three gallons, but I wasn't.

I don't care what anyone says folks is well-off. When I was a kid, you did well if you could feed your kids and put food on the table, clothes on their back. Not talking wardrobe full and Nike trainers. When we was kids, you had a set of clothes for school, and they did you all week. Monday morning at the Belfield household there was an old saying: 'first up, best dressed'. You picked your clothes for the week. Our Cliffy had to go to school in a lilac jumper for a week cos he was late up and everyone else hated it, and he was last up so it was his. I've seen lads go to school in shirts that they couldn't button, and we had big sloppies. You picked 'em for the week, and as soon as you got home, you had your work clothes. They was for the week. You was very lucky. There were kids at our school who didn't have as many clothes as us. There was one lad as went to school with us, he had shorts all the time cos he had one pair and that was it. They never got washed. He didn't come Monday with cleans like us. He had the same. Yet today, if kids haven't got a mobile phone, plasma TV and Sky, 'I've been abused'. But the younger folk are poorer … poor in spirit.

As far as I can see now, all my mother did was work. There was a big dinner for everybody, then we went off to play. We had to go t' bed at nine, earlier when we were little; at ten to nine, we were called in: 'Come and have your suppers.' We never stopped eating; what a job for my mother to be on tap to make all these meals – phenomenal.

All I look back on in my childhood is happiness. Christmas Eve, we were so excited we couldn't sleep. Same present every year: a pair of jeans and a pair of pyjamas. In a sock were an apple, an orange and some monkey nuts. I look back at my parents – they were star turns, my mum and dad were; they had waited up and it all happened. They were absolutely star characters. Everything happened when you were out of the house. We sang carols 'til 2 a.m. I bet they sat there thinking, 'I wish them buggers'd go to bed.' They did it all with a smile cos it was Christmas. ●

June evening. **Photo**: Sheila Hine.

PART 3
From buckets to bulk tanks
1970s to 1980s

Making hay; silage rye-grass monoculture; 'improving' the land; the decline of mixed farming; self-sufficient farms; old milking systems give way to the new; new breeds; joining the Common Market; subsidies and surpluses; milk quotas; changing the landscape; the Harpur Crewe Estate.

OVERLEAF: Cattle and swallow, September morning. **Photo**: Sheila Hine.

PART 3: FROM BUCKETS TO BULK TANKS
1970s to 1980s

The 1970s were a period of transition in British agriculture. The farming landscapes in lowland Britain were being transformed. Hedges were grubbed out, field sizes increased, and areas of permanent pasture were ploughed up for arable crops. The wildlife deserts of lowland south and east England with their prairie-like wheat fields are and were worlds away from the hills of the South West Peak, but pastoral landscapes across Britain were also on the cusp of change with new grassland management, new dairying systems, new breeds and increasing mechanisation. Nonetheless, change was still slow to come in upland areas where farming families largely kept to traditional methods on small mixed farms where the seasons, the weather, farm buildings, field size and terrain dictated how many animals could be kept and what could be grown.

In the South West Peak, many farmers continued to work in the ways their parents had done, with sheep on the hill, haymaking in summer, cows tied in shippons all winter and most fodder grown on the farm. There was a high level of self-sufficiency with modest outputs. Flower-rich hay meadows were once essential to stock farming, supplying winter fodder for sheep, cattle and horses. Hay meadows were a precious resource for wildlife as well as being places of great beauty, unique and particular to their localised soil, topography and aspect. Some meadows were hundreds of years in the making, with as many as fifty plant species in just one square metre and many more in total. They were a food source for a rich variety of insects, birds and animals, and provided cover for breeding and raising young. In the lower lying valleys of the South West Peak, traditional pastures and hay meadows had long dominated the scene. Other, typically rushy pastures had been grazed by sheep and cattle for centuries in an unchanged, unimproved condition. These varied kinds of permanent pastures contained many rare species and have been vital for ground-nesting birds.

In the 1970s, even in the South West Peak, traditional pastures started to be 'improved'. They were ploughed up or reseeded with perennial rye grass to be made into silage through a process of fermentation. Silage, usually stored in pits, is now often wrapped in plastic bales. The rye grasses that have replaced the traditional swards are fast growing and can be cut four or even five times a year; unlike hay, which produces just one crop that must be cut and dried and turned in the field before baling. Rye grass dominates and eliminates other species and is often treated with nitrogen-rich fertiliser to maintain its high output. This alters the composition of the soil, impacting micro-organisms and damaging soil life. The rye-grass monoculture does not support the level of insect life that waders, skylarks and partridge need to rear their young successfully, as beetles, larvae and invertebrates that are food for nestlings become scarcer.

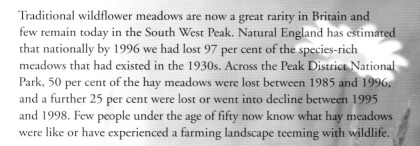

Traditional wildflower meadows are now a great rarity in Britain and few remain today in the South West Peak. Natural England has estimated that nationally by 1996 we had lost 97 per cent of the species-rich meadows that had existed in the 1930s. Across the Peak District National Park, 50 per cent of the hay meadows were lost between 1985 and 1996, and a further 25 per cent were lost or went into decline between 1995 and 1998. Few people under the age of fifty now know what hay meadows were like or have experienced a farming landscape teeming with wildlife.

As herds grew in size and more was demanded of the land, the labour-intensive work of haymaking and waiting for the right weather persuaded more and more farmers to give up on hay. The following accounts record the farming practices that persisted in parts of the South West Peak in the last century.

Meadow. **Photo**: Sheila Hine.

Denise Jarman

Denise Jarman was born in 1952 and grew up on Boosley Grange Farm near Longnor. She remembers life on the family farm up until the great changes of the 1980s and 1990s. She often revisits the farm, where most of the fields are now rented out to a large-scale dairy producer.

When I hear a lapwing, it just takes me back to one of my favourite memories. My sister Yvonne and I used to walk to school up the lane, and lapwings would nest on the pasture there every summer. That doesn't happen now because they've changed their habitat. They've changed that into a field that they now mow for silage, so we have no lapwings any more. There were large numbers that would come and fly down. We had to run the gauntlet every morning and every evening because they would just come and fly down and nearly touch your head. Their call is just amazing, and whenever I hear a lapwing, I always think of that part of my childhood.

I was born in 1952, and we sold the farm in 1979 after my father died. I've no bad memories of my childhood whatsoever. I think it was one of the happiest times of my life. And we were not that isolated, really, because I had lots of relations that lived around and I had a sister. I was sixteen months older than her, and she was my best friend. We played together all the time. We had jobs we had to do when we came back from school. We had to collect the eggs from henhouses all around the farm. We had to put the milk units together and collect the cows in the summer. As we grew up, our summer holidays were spent haymaking, driving a tractor – a Fordson Major. The clutch is high off the ground and we were only tiny, and we had to stand on this with two feet with all our weight to make it go. We'd be driving the tractor while they'd be loading the bales up. That was easy for us to do because we were not old enough to load. When we did get old enough, we had to stack and do all the haymaking jobs. That's how we spent all of our summer holidays. We had a lot of hay meadows.

'When I was young, I would have described our farm as having lush meadows with lots of wild flowers. I can't remember the last time ever I saw a meadow filled with wild flowers.'

Haymaking time at Sheldon House Farm, Brund, 2007. **Photo**: Sheila Hine.

All of the hedgerows have been taken out. There used to be three fields, possibly four, that used to be meadows, and now it's just one huge field. It makes it easier now, doesn't it? They've got huge tractors, whereas I can remember when we had a horse, a white horse called Dick, and he used to pull the trailer, but now it's all these huge machines. I can remember the hayricks, and where we used to position every hayrick in every field, and the horse being used to gather the hay on carts. We used to pitchfork it up onto the trailer. When my dad bought a baler, it was marvellous, so much easier. My sister and I would walk around the edges of every field and rake in all the last bits.

We had cows and sheep, never anything else. My dad never kept pigs, just cows and sheep. We had a Friesian herd with a few Guernseys and Jerseys just to keep the cream up. But the majority of them were Friesians. We kept more than twenty and they all had names.

I used to hate the winters because on a Saturday morning we would have to clean out all of the shippons with a wheelbarrow, a brush and a shovel. When the cows were in for winter, they were tied up in a shippon. Now they have huge sheds. They're not restrained. It's nicer obviously for the cow. I never thought about how a cow would feel just standing in the same position for about five or six months. If the weather was nice, my dad used to let them out into the yard and then put them back in. That was from November until the 1st of May because they had to protect the grass.

It could be beautiful weather, it could be fantastic weather, but my father never, ever let them out before the 1st of May. Even if you had a scorching April, they would be in. It was wonderful watching the cows being let out for the first time after the winter – they would just skip off and run around; they would be frolicking.

When I was young, I would have described our farm as having lush meadows with lots of wild flowers. I can't remember the last time ever I saw a meadow filled with wild flowers. The land, I think, was better cared for. The thistles were cut down and I know it sounds cruel, but if we had molehills, my Uncle Fred would try and eradicate the moles. Definitely the land was better cared for. My dad and Uncle Fred were great drystone wallers. If a wall fell down, they would build it back up every year. Yvonne and I used to go thistle spudding.[3]

The cows were tied up to a boskin. Even as a child, when we were milking, you would go up between them and milk them. We didn't have any problems with any cows because you were interacting with them all the time. You were feeding them hay twice a day, you were feeding them corn and you were cleaning the shippons out, not like today. ●

---

3 Thistle spudding was a laborious process of hand-digging thistles to below the root with a tool made for the job known as a spud. Such tools have been found dating back to Roman times.

Denise Jarman (nee Lownds) and Heather Fryer-Winder. **Photo**: Christine Gregory.

The ancient farmhouse at Boosley Grange is split in two, and the little girl next door to Denise and her family was Heather Fryer-Winder. Heather lived alone with her father David Fryer for twenty years after her mother left when she was just five years old. Heather left the farm in her twenties, but later returned to Boosley Grange, where she now lives with her husband, two children and father. David once had a large dairy herd, but most of the fields are now let for grazing. Heather remembers a tough and lonely life on the farm in which support from the girls next door was vital to her.

Heather Fryer-Winder

I was born here, and me dad was thirty when I was born. My mother was nineteen, and I'm now fifty-three. I was brought up just with me dad, so I remember it being quite tough as a child really, just me and me dad. And I remember sheep farming and prodding the snow with sticks looking for sheep, and things like that.

My dad would get up at half past six and have a cup of tea and bread and butter. Then he would go out and milk the cows, and then come in and have breakfast. I just took myself off to school. It was tough, walking up the lane and then to Eleven Lane Ends for school buses, and we used to have to walk back from where the bus dropped us off. It's quite a walk, but I was never on me own – there'd be a lot of children went in those days.

You learned how to work hard and graft, and how to use a brush. You just had to get your jobs done. You finished a job. I think that's how I am personally today. If I set out to do something, I'll finish it; whereas perhaps the youngsters today probably aren't like that. I think the young ones farming today, they just haven't got that same drive, they haven't got that knowledge that the older generation have. There's just young lads driving tractors, flying up and down, just doing what they've gotta do. They get home and they haven't experienced what it could be like.

I do love it around here. I love the countryside, but I always feel as though I've missed out on something. My children now are very sporty and I take them here, there and everywhere. I was very sporty as a young child, but I couldn't do these things because my father was dedicated to milking, lambing, whatever. Once, I was chosen to represent the school in athletics. It was this big event, and my father wouldn't take me because he was too busy. He wasn't interested. So I feel I missed out. I would've liked to have had a lot more of a social time, particularly as a teenager. Yvonne and Denise (next door) were older than me, and I latched on to them. I was very sad when they both got married and left and moved on. I was fourteen in '79, and Yvonne and Denise were my rock.

'You learned how to work hard and graft, and how to use a brush.'

When I was about twenty-five, I decided that I wanted to experience a bit more of the world, as I felt quite enclosed at the farm. I had lots of jobs to do, and I just needed to get away and experience a bit more. I was working in Buxton and my boss managed to get me a hotel job in Bad Nauheim in Germany, which is one of Buxton's twin towns. I met my husband from Glossop over there, and we came back to the farm when my son was eighteen months old.

I suppose I'm living my life through my children – how I wanted it to be. I see me in Abbie when I look at her doing her athletics. I definitely live what I wanted through my children. Seeing David at the weekend win a triathlon, it was fabulous.[4] I run myself; I love it – fell running. I think, 'Make the most of what you've got on your doorstep.' We'll probably stay here for a long time. ●

'Used to give 'em a name.'

Gilbert Shirley

Gilbert Shirley was born in 1944, and farms with his nephew at Waterhouse Farm near Longnor. Like so many others before them, they gave up the dairy herd in 2012 and now keep dairy heifers to sell at Leek Market, along with beef cattle and sheep. He has lived his entire life on the farm where he first started working over sixty years ago.

Soon as you got about nine or ten, you started helping, bringing cows in for milking, suckling two or three calves. Didn't know different. We had about twenty-eight cows. The cows used to come in them days with shouting. Used to give 'em a name; the name sorta stuck with that cow then, like Daisy, Buttercup, Andrea, and we used to call one Ted. The cows'd last 'til they were about ten years old. The milk cows, they learned t' go in their own stall. It takes them a while. They've got for t' learn, but they do learn. In winter, they just went out in the yard to drink. They'd jump round a bit, you put hay in and they'd come back in and you tied 'em up. We used to keep about eight calves, eight Friesian heifers, but you didn't have more cos you couldn't get 'em in in t' winter. I think they would like t' come in if the weather was rough; if it started freezing and a bit of snow coming. It were bit of a job. You had do 'em when they were little calves, tie them first time. In spring, they went like billy-o down t' field with their tails up. They run round for about two hours, then they settled down. I can't see anyone doing all that these days. Now you've got these big sheds, just bung 'em in and that's it. ●

---

4 Heather's son David Fryer-Winder has competed at some of the highest levels of his sport. He qualified for World Championships in 2018, and was placed high in European Sprint-Distance Triathlon Championships in 2017 and in 2018.

Gilbert Shirley. **Photo**: Christine Gregory.

Julia Cook. **Photo**: Christine Gregory.

Julia Cook

Julia Cook, Gilbert Shirley's niece, was born in the late 1960s and remembers the vital job the family had to do every summer.

If you managed to start before the beginning of July, I think that would be a very good year for hay. I think we were generally haymaking from about the second week in July. And depending on the weather, it would go on probably all through the school holidays and you'd be listening to the weather forecast on Radio 4 at five to six every day and trying to plan to mow and get it in while the weather was good. It's the main thing I remember about the summers, really – that the most important thing we had to do was get the hay in.

There were other farms locally that were starting to do silage by then. I don't remember any loose haystacks. It was all little bales, so the little yellow baler, which we don't have any more, was the key piece of kit. The first tractor that I was allowed to have a go on was a little Massey Ferguson 35, a red one. I used to drive when we were carting the hay, so that'd mean driving from bale to bale, pulling the hay cart. And then we used to go up on the hayloft to help with the unloading. When I was first old enough to go up there, it was all pitchforked onto the loft. So there was a lot of routine to it, and a lot of practice that had just been learned through doing it and through what we'd been told to do by Granddad.

The haymaking was done by the family. My job and my brothers' job was to get the hacking in from the wall sides. When the rowing-up was done, we raked where the rower missed the hay on the corners. There wasn't anything wasted. Everything was picked up and baled and no loose grass was left in a field. It's what your animals ate in the winter but I think it was more a sense of doing a good job and not leaving anything behind in the field.

My mum used to do the baling. Women were out doing, certainly at harvest time, and Mum had the role of keeping the dairy clean too. I don't know whether they'd remember hand-milking, but they'd remember milking with an engine, with a generator.

When I was growing up in the '70s, we used to tie animals over here for the winter, 'o'er at barn'. And so Mum used to walk across here before she took us to school, to fodder them. There's no water bowls in here, so they'd go out to the well, which is in the barn yard there, to drink once a day. The stalls are different widths in different places for different sized animals – the heifer shippon at the top end, the bing in the middle, and the stirk stalls and calf stalls at the bottom. I suppose in most barns, the interior structure will have gone altogether, or it will have rotted away to the point where it isn't useable any more. ●

'The most important thing we had to do was get the hay in.'

Field barn on Waterhouse Farm. **Photo**: Sheila Hine.

The old field barn on Waterhouse Farm demonstrates exactly how animals were kept from the 1800s. **Photo**: Christine Gregory.

Helen Heathcote

Helen was born in the 1950s, and her family farmed at Pyegreave Farm in Cheshire. She was the last farmer in her extended family, and until recently she kept beef stock on the smallholding at Bottom House in Staffordshire where she now lives. Helen remembers how her parents' farm business kept going for decades with a high degree of self-sufficiency and no subsidies. In addition to sustaining the family, her parents' milk round helped sustain the local community by providing social support as well as the daily milk delivery.

When I was younger, we didn't have that many cows or that many sheep, but we had a vast milk round, and we bottled all our own milk. It wasn't pasteurised. It was the raw milk. It was TT [tuberculin tested]. We used to grow so much of our own produce to feed the animals. I can remember turning the mangold chopper, cos we grew those. We kept fields and fields of kale. Kale is en vogue to eat now, but we used to cut it in the winter and feed it to the cows, and we used to have a lot of brewer's grains. So it wasn't all coming through the farm gate. It was produced on site.

Our family moved from Rainow to Langley because the weather was harsh up there. It didn't suit Grandma's health, so they bought something relatively sheltered. It's virtually all moorland round there, all barren. When they moved to Pyegreave Farm (where I grew up), the land was so beautiful, the ground, the soil. We even had our own stream,

Helen Heathcote. **Photo**: Christine Gregory.

'You shouldn't really have to rely on subsidies to farm, should you?'

Helen's father, Joe ... Barber with Toby the horse on the milk round at Langley with chapel in background. **Photo**: Cyril Dawson, local historian (deceased)

a watercourse that was so pure, it grew watercress. My dad used to gather up bags and bags of the watercress.

Dad always worked on the farm with his brother and his sisters. The farm supported the whole family – five children. They all worked there. When the girls got older, they did perhaps secretarial courses, but the boys stayed and they farmed together until my dad and his brother retired. We lived there when my grandparents retired. When we left the farm in 1990, the family had been there seventy years.

There was a big orchard and we were growing apples and plums. We grew fields of potatoes as well. We sold the potatoes on the milk round, and the eggs, of course. We had quite a lot of hens. My dad didn't just sell milk. It used to take him so long to do his milk round because he'd be turning people's mattresses or taking Mrs Jones's coal order to the coal man. We left when he retired. When he sold it, they had a big party in the village for him. He went 365 days a year. On Christmas Day and Boxing Day, he would dress up. He would make his own costumes – he would be Rupert Bear; he was the Mad Hatter. He was just amazing.

There was another farmer in the next village that used to do a milk round. He bought ours when we finished. The other farmer, I think he bought his milk in. We did everything. We bottled and produced ours on the farm. Before we had the vans, we had Toby the horse, and if Dad was

too long at one place, Toby used to know where the next slice of bread was, and he would go on his own; and woe betide Dad if he was in a house if it thundered, because Toby would go home.

We always had British Friesians – a closed herd. If we ever bought anything in, it died. We never, never had TB. You used to get red and white Friesians as well. They are so hardy. The longevity – they went on for years. Our young stock were never housed. I remember we had a really bad blizzard. We had to get the Land Rover out and we went to look for the cows. They had gone down a ravine near the river. There wasn't any snow down there. They were under the trees and they were absolutely fine. They always produced a big coat.

Mum would do all the bottling of the milk; then after lunch, when my dad came back, she would wash all the bottles, feed the hens, weigh potatoes up. He used to sell cigarettes, so she went to Macclesfield to the wholesalers to get those. But on wet days, it was awful on the milk round. They would see you and they would say, 'Can I have five pounds of potatoes?' So you would go back. 'Can I have half a dozen eggs? Can I have twenty cigarettes?' You would go back and you would get wetter and wetter.

We sold full-cream milk. It just went straight through the cooler, the old-fashioned sort. The water used to run through. We were very lucky. We had got a natural spring, so water wasn't a problem. We'd got in churn coolers.

Mum had a wooden dairy. We never had anything rejected. They used to come and spot-check you when Dad was out on the round – take a bottle and sample it. We never had a problem.

When our cows were housed in the winter, they were tied by the neck. When it was really cold, my dad used to pop something in the latch holes. You couldn't have draughts. It was just like a sauna – it used to steam. If you did that with these new cowsheds, they would just get pneumonia and die.

The farm was on a hillside, in a valley. The house was at the top of the yard. All round, we had coppices, woods, streams. It was idyllic, really. There was a footpath that went over to Macclesfield to the golf links. It was dry ground – not like round here where you are wading through bogs. We just had so many wild flowers all the time. There was always something growing. There were many birds, kingfishers where the streams were. It was wooded – it was very secluded. We had got badger setts up on the top, but they weren't a problem. They didn't have TB. We had wild orchids on our ground, so nothing was intensive.

We were making hay, always made hay even when he was silaging. We made some hay because young stock do better on hay. It's easier to feed calves hay. Ours was clamped silage, but we always made hay on the hottest days. My dad was one of those who used to screw the baler up, so the bales were just like lead. I can never remember getting a bale out

in the winter and it being mouldy. Some people don't know how to make hay; some say, 'That's too green.' If it's June hay, it will be green and it will be the best hay you will ever have had. You want to eat it yourself.

They didn't get up that early – seven o'clock to go and get the cows in to milk. Dad would come in. He'd leave his brother to get on with milking. As soon as there was milk ready, Mum would go start and do all the bottling and then come up. She would cook breakfast for everybody and then go do the hens. She was just working all the time. At the same time, she had her dad's farm at Wildboarclough. Her mum had died and she had some brothers, so she did all their washing. She went and cleaned up after them. She is still living; she was ninety-one last week. She's amazing. She is as fit as me. Dad had to retire because his hips went. He just worked himself to death.

The biggest thing for us was when quotas came in. You were allocated, so when we sold the farm, the quota was sold as a separate entity; that was sold on its own. The more quota you had, the more you could milk. That's when herds started to increase in size – the first nail in the coffin. Then getting rid of the MMB [Milk Marketing Board] as well. You knew you had a cheque every month. It did go up and down, as it does now. But when we were farming, we farmed and we didn't have subsidies. There were no subsidies when my dad farmed; there were no subsidies when he left. You shouldn't really have to rely on subsidies to farm, should you? ●

JOINING THE COMMON MARKET

The Common Agricultural Policy (CAP), established in 1962, was one of the founding policies of the European Economic Community (EEC, now European Union (EU)). It was aimed at providing food security for the people of the member states and financial support for farmers which guaranteed prices for their products. The further aims were to promote productivity with technological advances and to stabilise markets and prices for consumers. The wholesale embracing of these aims consolidated the earlier productivity drive of the war years.

When the UK joined the Common Market in 1973, subsidies changed the culture of much of rural Britain and led to the increasing industrialisation of farming. Overproduction quite quickly resulted in massive surpluses and stockpiles: the so-called milk lakes, butter, beef and wheat mountains. Down the years, many CAP reforms have reflected global concerns and changing priorities in land use; but from the late 1970s, when it was clear that subsidised milk production increasingly outstripped consumer demand, reforms were directed at limiting supplies. From 1984, EEC member states were fined heavily if they produced too much milk, and the levy paid was to be recovered from farmers who had overproduced.

Milk quotas were introduced in the UK in 1984, and each dairy farmer was allocated a production limit. This was normally attached to land, but quotas became a transferable, saleable or leasable asset – which was not the intention of the EEC. The trading of quotas has been just one aspect of the increasingly complicated business of dairy farming. Originally introduced for a period of five years, quotas were maintained until 2015. Milk quotas caused problems for some farmers with too little capacity, and some farmers who could not afford to buy or lease sufficient quota to make a living were driven out of the dairy industry. Some remained in farming but switched to sheep or beef cattle to balance the farm books with European subsidies then paid per head.

Graham and Carol Turnock. **Photo**: Sheila Hine.

Graham Turnock

Graham was born in 1958, and has spent his life farming at Dun Lea Farm near Onecote. His lifetime of farming reflects the general drive to expand and intensify, thereby increasing inputs and yields.

Dad was born here; Granddad farmed here before him. Granddad was born at Dairy House, Horton and then moved up to here, then me dad was born here. It was eighty-four acres. Granddad had got six cows, half a dozen pigs, a few sheep, hens – a few of everything. I think they grew a bit of corn in the war years cos they had to. I were born in 1958.

Dad started farming on his own around 1960. It was just a family farm making a living. In the '70s, he started to expand with a bulk tank and cubicle shed that had gone up in 1969. Before that, he had shippons; never had a pipeline, but he went from milking in the buckets to the parlour. That was about 1970 or '71. We milked around sixty then, which were quite a big herd in them days. Things were changing. We kept increasing the cows, I remember the hundredth cow on the place. That would be early '70s. We kept buying land from '70s. Dad bought a neighbouring farm, which took us up to 120 acres, and a bit of land off the next neighbour. Kept going from there.

Quotas came in a year we were expanding and hit us hard. They allocated us an extra 70,000 litres. We bought 1.5 million litres of quota in the next ten years. First lot we bought were thirty pence a litre. We also used to lease in. That got to twenty-odd pence, I think – stupid price. We did buy some at seventy pence, then we bought some later on when it started coming down to about eighteen to twenty pence a litre. Looking back, it wasted a lot of money, especially on leasing, but we had to do it. Needed to do it to stay in. We were expanding – what else do you do? We had to do it, but it was taking a lot of money all the year. Quotas kept the price of milk up. As soon as quotas ended, look what happened to prices. So I think they was a good thing.

Late '80s, we started expanding the sheep. Two next-door neighbours wanted us to rent the land, so we rented it and put sheep on. Since then, that land's gone, but we bought our own, so the sheep are on our own land now. We had about 340 sheep in the early '90s. Now we are up to about 900 breeding ewes, mainly mules. We do keep a few Texel cross mules each year, ewe lambs; they come out of the flock. We like our mules cos they are good mothers; they just have too many lambs. ●

'Quotas kept the price of milk up.'

Brian Wainwright. **Photo**: Sheila Hine.

'It's a dangerous job on your own.'

Brian Wainwright

Brian farms at Parkhouse Farm, Meerbrook. He describes the big change from milking in a shippon to a modern parlour.

The main change in the '70s for us was going from old cowsheds into the new cowshed. When I first started when I was thirteen, we were in the old cowsheds. I remember milking into churns. After me dad had died, I was milking in the shippon on my own. It's a dangerous job on your own. I know there was a few times when I was scrambling from under a cow that I'd got kicked with, so that's why after me dad had died, I looked at putting a parlour in. It was New Year's Eve 1974 when we started in the new building which tied thirty up each side. It totally changed the system. Then we went loose-housed on straw with a biggish feed area inside, put four bales of silage in. We keep fifty cows in the main building and the rest down the yard, and milked through an 8/16 herringbone parlour.[5] For my number of cows, that's a big parlour, so I don't spend too long milking.

We were milking mainly Friesian types. Not really into the big tall leggy sorts. I like a good Friesian-type cow. I know some folk get 10,000 litres a cow, but if I can get five and a half thousand litres, that will do me, if the price is right.

[5] A herringbone parlour would allow eight cows each side to be milked along diagonal lines.

The biggest changes were mechanisation and technology – going into bulk tank. I suppose we made hay 'til about 1991 or '92, then we made silage. We went all on to big-baled silage. We're still on big-bale silage. We make some round-bale hay as well. I only make little-bale hay if we have got help; it's more of a novelty doing that. I have still got a small baler, but I don't use it. I think it's vintage at the back of the shed now. We only do 400 bales of hay now. We have some friends who keep a few sheep and some donkeys. I pay them with thirty bales of hay if we do 400 bales, and they jump at that and they come and help us and have a drink of wine.

Folk were doing all sorts when quotas come in as I remember – drying cows off to get down to the quotas. I think in the end, though, quotas were a good thing. Now quotas are gone again, it seems like some folk are getting really mad, and you get this flooding of the market now. We've just had two years of hard going, which is difficult, but it is picking up now [in 2017]. I think there's going to be a lot of milk this summer; the price will be coming down – we will have to wait and see again. ●

Shippon at Waterhouse Farm. **Photo**: Christine Gregory.

Frank Belfield

Frank Belfield explains how the funding system was open to abuse and distorted farming practices, but says it could also be a lifesaver for hard-pressed hill farmers.

Early '80s, the quotas had come in on the milk job. When that came in, that upset sheep job because folks who were on good ground and didn't get a good enough milk quota bought a lot of broken-mouth ewes. They flooded the market with lambs off sheep as should have been in Sheffield abattoir. The country was saturated wi' sheep. It didn't get abused legally, but it got abused against what it was meant to do. You should never tar everybody with the same brush. There was lot of sheep kept because of the sub – old broken-mouth ewes at back end that ought to a' been gone. Well, they were only worth an odd quid or two – 'Oh, jigger 'em – we'll let 'em run round and draw the sub, and then they can go' – whether they'd had a lamb or not. As long as the counting man saw 'em on the appropriate day. The land got overstocked by that. It got overeaten. Just purely overstocked – just chasing the sub. You know, it was the carrot and stick thing again. ●

'The country was saturated wi' sheep.'

Suffolk sheep with Hen Cloud in background. **Photo**: Sheila Hine.

BEEF CATTLE SUBSIDIES
Frank Belfield

The beef cattle subsidy made it as you could just about afford to keep 'em. There was no profit; it was only in the hopes of having a better do the next year. The subsidies carried us over until things got better and we could go again. In '73, when things were that bad, calves were a pound a piece in the auctions. Steer sub were eighteen pounds in '73. It stayed on for a few years; when stock went dearer, it faded away, but it got us out of trouble. Inputs were ridiculously dear; corn was quite expensive. '72 wasn't a very good summer, and there was a lot of poor hay and a lot of corn got lost. Nobody wanted buy stock because they hadn't got the fodder or the corn to feed 'em with, so them as had reared 'em were stuck with 'em because as a crop when we've got 'em ready, they've got to go, an't they? We hadn't got buildings winter 'em.

It didn't matter which way you wriggled and turned, there were no escape. Them as 'ad got stock had to buy expensive feed cos them as 'adna got the feed werena goin' buy stock!

Suckler cow subsidy was one o' the best things they ever did because it give you that incentive to keep the herd together. It were only Angus and Hereford, in that day; Limmy [Limousin] were just comin' in, but you'd still got a proper beef animal that could finish on grass, which was another bonus; whereas anything out of a dairy cow, you needed get in the corn bag. I think they should never have let the hill cow sub go. It was taking subsidy off 'em as jiggered 'em. ●

'In '73 … calves were a pound a piece in the auctions.'

THE HARPUR CREWE ESTATE

In the sixteenth century, the Harpur Crewe family, through wealth and marriage, began to build a huge estate that in its heyday stretched from Warslow in Staffordshire to Calke Abbey in South Derbyshire – a distance of forty miles, covering three counties. The first Baronet, Sir Henry Harper, acquired Calke in 1622, and a succession of baronets and their descendants held this and the country shooting estate in north Staffordshire into the twentieth century. From the First World War,

NORTH STAFFORDSHIRE

In the Parishes of Quarnford, Heathylee Hollinsclough and Warslow and Elkstones, Five Miles South-west of Buxton, and Eight Miles from Leek.

Particulars, Plans and Conditions of Sale of
A VALUABLE AGRICULTURAL ESTATE

A PORTION OF

The Harpur Crewe
North Staffordshire Estate

Extending to about

9,357 ACRES

comprising

125 DAIRY and GRAZING FARMS from 20 to 215 Acres
NUMEROUS SMALLHOLDINGS
A LICENSED INN WITH LAND
COUNTRY COTTAGES   ACCOMMODATION LAND, Etc.

To be offered for Sale by Auction unless previously disposed of by Private Treaty on

MONDAY, 16th JULY, 1951 (LOTS 1 to 73)
TUESDAY, 17th JULY, 1951 (LOTS 74 to 149)
WEDNESDAY, 18th JULY, 1951 (LOTS 150 to 212)

at the TOWN HALL, BUXTON,

At 11 a.m. and 2.30 p.m.   by

MESSRS. W. S. BAGSHAW & SONS

(G. Fletcher Bagshaw, M.B.E., F.A.I., S. H. Bagshaw, M.B.E., F.A.I., W. R. Bagshaw, F.A.I., J. L. Bagshaw, F.A.I.)

Solicitors :
Messrs. TAYLOR, SIMPSON & MOSLEY,
St Mary's Gate, DERBY.
(Tel 46006).

Land Agent :
C. C. PRESTON, Esq., F.L.A.S.,
Estate Office, TICKNALL, Nr. DERBY.
(Tel. Melbourne 3142).

Auctioneers :
Messrs. W. S. BAGSHAW & SONS,
Vine House, ASHBOURNE (Tel. 221,
and at Uttoxeter, Bakewell and Derby.

Sale brochure for Harpur Crewe Estate.

the estate went into decline, and various parts of it were disposed of from the 1920s onwards after the death of the tenth and last baronet. In the twentieth century, the break-up of the Harpur Crewe Estate provided opportunities for local people to acquire their own homes, land and farms in a way that is almost unique to this area. In July 1951, 9,357 acres (3,787 hectares) of the Harpur Crewe north Staffordshire estate were sold in 212 separate lots. Over a period of three days, cottages, parcels of land, dairy and grazing farms, a licensed inn and many smallholdings were disposed of.

In the 1980s, following the death of Charles Harpur Crewe, the family owed death duties they were unable to pay, and their remaining estate was 'gifted' to the nation. Calke Abbey was given to the National Trust, and the Warslow Moors Estate was given to the Peak District National Park. On page 95, Chris Manby from the Peak District National Park Authority outlines the problems and opportunities presented by this acquisition.

The sales of 1951 gave a start or a boost to many farming families. Much of the land is not prime farmland. It includes some of the lower-valley pastoral land described by the dairy farmers in this part of the book, but there were also some upland farms with rough grazing on difficult boggy, marginal land. Michael and Sylvia Woolley and Geoff and Margaret Tunnicliffe describe their early years working to make their upland farms productive.

Michael and Sylvia Woolley farmed at Big Fernyford near Longnor, a farm now partly owned by the Peak District National Park Authority and Natural England and occupied by Neil Richardson (see page 146).

Michael Woolley

I went down to Big Fernyford in 1968, and Mother and Dad went to Little Fernyford. We got married the following July. Previously it'd been owned by the Harpur Crewe Estate. I think all those farms round there were Harpur Crewe. It hadn't got a dairy licence on it because the people who lived there had just had sheep. You had to have a borehole put in so you could get clean water, and you paid a licence for that too – four pounds something a year, which was a lot of money. It was a spring that was there before.

Michael and Sylvia Woolley. **Photo**: Christine Gregory.

We had to do all that before we moved down there. There was no electricity either at start, and we had to have that brought across. '70s, I had it all drained. We had a big firm come and did it all properly, and then when we left and somebody else were there, Peak Park wanted know where the drains were and block 'em all up. So it just went from one extreme to the other, but that's the way of it – evolution, isn't it? If you look back through history, one generation have made something, the others have messed it up, haven't they?

We only milked about thirty when we moved there for a start, but when we packed up, we were milking a hundred nearly. When we were haymaking, there were only me and t' neighbours. It was full of black grouse and birds and tufts of grass. By the time you've drained it, mucked it, farmed it, it got nesher and nesher. It involved a lot of work as you're building the herd more and more, and then it just got on top of us and I just couldna do it, so I packed it up. It's a big job on your own, takes some doing. ●

'Staffordshire's bogshire. You're fighting a losing battle all the time.'

Sylvia Woolley

Michael's dad had rented from the Duke of Devonshire and always wanted to buy a farm. So he bought one down there. Daftest thing he ever did, really – to move from Derbyshire to Staffordshire – really silly move. Staffordshire to Derbyshire's a better way round; Derbyshire land's so much better than Staffordshire; that's just bogs and rushes. But you can't see these things when you're young, can you? Now that we're old, we can see. You should've run the other way as fast as ever you coulda gone, really. I love Staffordshire – I've lived in it ever since I've been married; but to farm up there in all those rushes and all that bog and all those gnats, and I think to meself I must have been absolutely crackers. Now they pay people to let it go; but when we went, it was the opposite way round. You could get a grant to drain it so that you were making the land better, improving it. It was nothing but rushes when we went there, but now it's going back to the moors as fast as ever it can. ●

'Daftest thing he ever did – to move from Derbyshire to Staffordshire.'

OVERLEAF: Cotton grass on Warslow Moors Estate. **Photo**: Sheila Hine.

Geoff and Margaret Tunnicliffe. **Photo**: Christine Gregory.

Geoff Tunnicliffe

Geoff and Margaret farm together with their son on Manor Farm in the Dane Valley.

Mum and Dad were married in 1938 and took Manor Farm over from Mum's parents. They rented the farm from Crewe and Harpur Estate until 1952, when they bought it. Manor Farm was about 125 acres and Dad built it up. He used to milk about thirty cows and had about fifty sheep, and he always bought a new car. All he had there was himself and a worker plus me when I got old enough, and that's all there is now.

'Back then, you could start in a little way and build up.'

When I left school, there was lads used to come out of the town and work on farms and finished up with their own farm. That could never happen now. You would have to have a father who was a multimillionaire to do it. Back then, you could start in a little way and build up; twenty-five cows would be nothing nowadays. There is so much you have to earn before you start living; there are so many expenses you have no control over. In those days, you could start on a very small farm and help someone else to get some money together. Odd bits of land became available as the old farmers died off on the small farms.

The first thing I can remember from when I left school fifty-five years ago is we used to spend all our spare time draining: digging up stone drains, clearing them out. Then we put so many pipe drains in to dry the land out so it'd make it more productive. And we used to do all our stone wall building. We used to put lime on and slag.[6] As we built more cattle up, we improved. We put the farmyard manure on, and we did improve it a lot. It made a big difference. I mean, one cow in them days would make a big difference and we improved the land so we could keep a few more sheep. You didn't borrow money, but if you made a bit, it stopped with you.

'The trouble with hay …'

I can remember Dad mowing with horses, and then he bought a tractor in 1947. It used to be all handwork. My great-grandfather planted a tree at the corner of every hay field for them to have their tea under. We used to make loose hay, cart it back and put it in the shed. In them days, you didn't ring the merchant up and say, 'I want ten ton of hay.' You managed with what you'd got, and if you can improve land, you can make a bit more hay. If you're going to make hay, you can't put fertiliser on – it makes it very hard to get dry. We put a complete fertiliser on so you grew probably a third more grass, which you could make into silage. You've a lot more guarantee than you did with hay. The trouble with hay, you can mow a perfectly good crop, and within four to five days it can be completely ruined by the weather because you've got to have three to four good days to get it dry, and that was the big thing. You couldn't afford to risk making poor hay, but you were pretty well guaranteed to make good silage. We got to the stage where we had to increase and we couldn't. Silage was one of the biggest things to get to be more productive.

---

6 Slag was a by-product of the steel industry used together with or as a substitute for limestone in agricultural applications to 'improve' acidic land.

There is some quite good land in the valley. Then we had thirty acres of meadow and probably another thirty or forty acres decent pasture. The rest was rough pasture. We made a living, didn't borrow money because you couldn't borrow money. You buy one piece of land and then another. We own about 280 acres now, plus we rent another 670 acres because we run on the Roaches estate. The farm is 900 feet above sea level and Manor Farm runs up to 1,100 feet, and of course the Roaches are 1,500 feet. We're definitely upland farmers.

MILKING – CHANGING SYSTEMS

Cows'd be in for six months and out for six months. Then the in-thing was cubicles and parlour milking. So we had another shed up. Me and the workman put cubicles in and had a milking parlour about thirty years ago. We've been having problems, because if you have cubicles, you finish up with a lot of slurry, so we had problems with the slurry being close to the river. We had one bit of a mishap. We've done well since we've gone onto loose housing where we bed the cows down on deep bedding, and we don't get the amount of slurry with straw beds.

We went into British Friesians for twenty-odd years and then we bought a Shorthorn. We've gone to pedigree Shorthorns and I wouldn't have anything different. There's nothing wrong with a British Friesian, but the Holstein Friesian – the longevity of them is two and a half lactations.[7] If you had a cow give 5,000 litres years ago, you had a belting good cow; and now they have to give 10,000 litres. It's like a car – if you do 50,000 miles or if you do 100,000 miles, it'll be worn out, won't it? I think we've had one had thirteen calves and the average is about eight or nine. With a Shorthorn, you can put any bull on it you like; and with a beef bull, you'd have a cracking good beef animal. Now we're on the Roaches, we have to run breeds 'at risk', that's Beef Shorthorn and Derbyshire Gritstone sheep.[8] So we have got quite a lot of Beef Shorthorns now. We've still also got Dairy Shorthorns. I don't think you can beat 'em. They are more suitable here, because they have to walk quite a way to the fields. We have six and half thousand litres from them.[9] •

7 A heifer (young cow) is often pregnant for the first time at fifteen months and has its first calf at two years, after nine months' gestation. A lot of cattle may be older than this. To keep producing milk, they then have a calf each year, which amounts to a lactation period of ten months per year. The number of lactations equates to the life of a cow before slaughter, which in this case would be just four years. The natural lifespan of a cow is twenty-five years.

8 These are breeds of farm animals that have their history and origins in the UK that meet the criteria specified in the EU's rural development regulations. These traditional breeds were once part of the rural land-scape and are now considered 'at risk' of extinction without special conservation measures. Such breeds are specially adapted to traditional farmland habitats, and are often considered to have less damaging environmental impacts, as they do well on fewer inputs. For example, many cattle browse on brambles, shrubs and herbs, and do not just graze on grass. There is subsidy for farming these breeds under current agri-environment schemes.

9 For more information about litres per cow per year, see pages 110 and 167.

Geoff and Margaret Tunnicliffe's Shorthorns at the Roaches. **Photo**: Sheila Hine.

Chris Manby

Chris Manby works for the Peak District National Park Authority as Rural Property and Visitor Experience Development Officer. He has worked with tenants on the Harpur Crewe Warslow Estate since it was first given over to the National Park in 1982.

'Tourism stops at Hartington and starts again at the Roaches.'

What eventually came to us was about thirteen main farm holdings, thirteen cottages and a church at Reapsmoor with a schoolroom underneath it, lots and lots of field barns, about ten blocks of woodland and then lots of blocks of moorland. Before our ownership, these were used for grouse shooting, and that was the main occupation of the Harpur Crewe family up until the late '70s, I suspect. We suddenly had a pub as well – the Royal Cottage on the Leek–Buxton road. So it was a very mixed portfolio – a traditional estate, and I think there are sixty or seventy different sorts of tenants with their grazing licences and mowing licences. The main land holding is in and around Warslow. You can imagine if you were the Harpur Crewe family having to sell off land, you sell off the bits further away from your house first. So around Warslow Hall, that was the last bit to go, and it was probably some of the more productive land.

The quality of the land in the Staffordshire moorlands area particularly is not that great, and I think it would be fair to say that over the generations, the Harpur Crewe family did little in the way of altering or improving the land. There was one exception back in the 1730s – Sir George Harpur Crewe tried to agriculturally improve the lot of the tenants and the quality of the land by enclosing. He was the one that did all the walls round the moorlands, but he died around 1750. I think his son did a bit, but after that, it seemed to revert to the wild. When the '50s and '60s post-war era came, the Harpur Crewe Estate weren't big into investment in the estates. They did do stuff – one or two new farm buildings – but it wasn't much. What we actually inherited was a fairly unmodernised estate. In one way, that was a bad thing; but in another way, it was an excellent thing for us because a lot of the estate missed out on post-war ploughing and draining, reseeding and all that sort of stuff, although the land there isn't ideally suited to that anyway. But it did mean that on the land side of things, a lot of the hay meadows and rough pastures and the moorland really survived without large-scale agricultural improvement. And although there were some new farm buildings, a lot of them were still very traditional, unmodernised houses, unmodernised stone barns. People were still milking in shippons and old cow sheds. It was a very labour-intensive type of work and, as I understand it, the policy was sort of: 'Yeah, we'll put investment in, but not a lot.' But the rents, you know, were kept reasonable to reflect that.

The designation of the Leek Moors Site of Special Scientific Interest (SSSI) was based mainly on the wading bird population. I've always loved it. I've always felt that it's just a quiet rural area within the national park. It's not a big touristy area. I always say, rightly or wrongly, tourism stops at Hartington and starts again at the Roaches.

EARLY DAYS OF PEAK DISTRICT NATIONAL PARK MANAGEMENT

People were living in fairly basic housing. There were one or two properties that were still on that lovely old term: 'night soil' collection. There were lots of stories about the farm buildings and how hard it was. They were powering out muck from old shippons, and people didn't have good manure stores, so it was all very hard work. We took a very pragmatic approach at the time, and thought the best thing to do was sort out living conditions for human beings, regardless of the conservation side of things. A priority really in those early days was just to get the domestic housing up to the best standard that we possibly could, and secondly to start providing some sort of more modern farm buildings that would make domestic life and working life much more efficient. That has been a process over thirty years, but we cracked off with the highest priority ones in the first ten or fifteen years. We charge 85 per cent of the market rent, and the whole ethos of that is to try and keep the domestic properties within a band that local people can afford.

Belted Galloway, a breed often used for conservation grazing, on heather moorland. **Photo**: Sheila Hine.

I would say pretty much every single domestic tenant on the estate is what I would call a local working person. There's no commuters or business people. ●

Shutlingsloe. **Photo**: Sheila Hine.

Dairy herd on a June evening with Hen Cloud on skyline. **Photo**: Sheila Hine.

PART 4
Winners and losers
1990s to 2018

BSE, foot-and-mouth disease and TB; the price of milk; wildlife losses; farming for conservation; waders in the South West Peak.

Carl Turnock baling hay near the Roaches. **Photo**: Sheila Hine.

PART 4: WINNERS AND LOSERS
1990s to 2018

There have been several crises in British farming over recent decades that have shaken both the industry and its public image. Farmers all over Britain have had to contend with tragic disease outbreaks and a constantly changing picture of rising costs and lower prices. In addition, climate change, extreme weather, degradation of landscapes, soils and water quality, and increasing global alarm at accelerating species loss have led to changing priorities over land use for both the British government and the European Union. The last thirty years have seen some gains for farmers and many losses. At the same time, counting the cost of intensive farming to the natural world has prompted a fundamental change of approach to the system of government and EU rewards and subsidies. This is the subject of the second part of this chapter. The immense difficulties in farming caused by disease epidemics and stagnating milk prices are explored first.

THE IMPACT OF DISEASE ON FARMING IN THE SOUTH WEST PEAK

Farmed animals have always been vulnerable to contagion – especially with modern systems and long-distance transportation. These factors made the devastating outbreak of foot-and-mouth disease at the start of the twenty-first century so much worse than that of 1967. It affected all stock farmers, even if, like those in the South West Peak, they were free of the disease.

Alan Dickinson

Alan works for the National Farmers' Union as the Group Secretary covering the Staffordshire Moorlands, based in the local office in Leek. He comes from a farming family in Northumberland and used to shear sheep for a living. He now owns a small farm of twenty-five acres, renting a further thirty acres at Rushton Spencer, four miles north of Leek.

Not long after I started at the NFU in 2000, we had the big foot-and-mouth epidemic in February 2001. That always puts a shiver down my spine whenever I think of it. They were horrendous times. We were the shoulder to cry on sometimes. It's amazing how people kept going in those times. We were very fortunate. We weren't affected in this area. In Uttoxeter and further over, they did have foot-and-mouth, but it was equally as bad in some ways that we didn't have it. My brother at home in Northumberland was within one farm of the disease, and he thinks now perhaps he'd have been better off if they'd been culled. He fought to the end not to be culled. His neighbours who were culled had good compensation packages, they had new sheds put up, new vehicles. It does make you wonder.

Alan Dickinson. **Photo**: Sheila Hine.

Livestock prices were very poor. There was a welfare scheme. Farmers didn't have feed. Livestock was away from the main holding and farmers couldn't get them back. There was a scheme where a lot of stock was culled – that kept some people going. Farmers got paid on the set value, so it didn't matter how good or bad they were. A scheme's a scheme. Some people benefit from it. Some would be embarrassed and ashamed to admit they'd done that. Only recently, I remember hearing of some very good farmers who got rid of a lot of poor stock. People were restocking after foot-and-mouth, but they weren't costing a great deal. They'd still get them fairly cheaply compared to the compensation packages they had. •

'We were the shoulder to cry on.'

The foot-and-mouth epidemic of 2001 devastated the farming community, with 2,000 cases reported across the country and the eventual slaughter of around ten million sheep and cattle. The images of burning pyres will remain in the minds of all those who watched the television news through the summer and autumn of 2001. By October, the costs to the agricultural and supply industries and to the outdoor leisure industries was estimated at eight billion pounds. The psychological cost to some in the farming community was incalculable, and the new century began with a bleak aspect for British farming. The industry had already taken a massive hit with the BSE crisis of the 1980s and 1990s.

BSE (bovine spongiform encephalopathy), commonly known as mad cow disease, is a fatal degenerative condition in cattle affecting the brain and spinal cord. Alarming neurological symptoms started appearing in cattle in the mid-1980s and became identified as BSE. In 1996, a link was made between the cattle disease and a new form in humans known as new variant Creutzfeldt–Jakob disease (nvCJD). The official view was that the disease in cattle was caused by their ingestion of contaminated meat and bonemeal (MBM) in some concentrate feeds, and that nvCJD could be caused by eating contaminated beef. By 2014, 177 people had died from a disease attributable to a 'species jump' from BSE. However, many farmers and independent researchers believe that the main contributing factors were environmental toxins such as the compulsory use of high-dose organophosphate insecticides used to treat cattle for warble flies. At the same time, cattle were also being fed on cereals from grain-mountain stores, often repeatedly treated with OP insecticides.

Independent researcher Mark Purdey pointed out major flaws in the official line on BSE. His research showed that hundreds of thousands of tons of the same MBM were exported to many countries for cattle feed which remained BSE-free. Also, no cattle born on organic farms (despite using MBM at that time) developed BSE. There have been hundreds of cases of BSE in cattle born since MBM was banned from use in animal feed.

BSE caused a tremendous upheaval in farming and allied industries. For several years, cattle over the age of thirty months when slaughtered were not allowed into the food chain. The height of the crisis hit in the early 1990s, and eventually nearly 4.5 million cattle were slaughtered after 180,000 animals were found to be affected. There was a worldwide ban on British beef which China did not lift until 2018.

Graham Turnock

Graham Turnock remembers what happened when cattle on his farm developed BSE in the early 1980s.

We had a few cases of BSE in home-bred cattle. They were born '78, I think. It were a shock, really, cos we was hoping we didn't get any. It was horrible to see these cows, all one group – one year's calves reared on straw. We had this adviser saying, 'Rear them on straw and give them these protein pellets', which we did. Two years later, then, they went daft. It was all one group of these cattle. Most of them went with it. They went and then it was cleared up. Wouldn't want that again. Once seen, never forgotten. Barren cows especially. Used to take them up to Redferns [abattoir]. It was a waste. Nothing were proven, no connection. I can remember that Professor Lacey coming on television said we were all going to die. Where's he gone? Frightened us to death, didn't he? I go to market, I have breakfast down there, had bacon and sausage every week – now it's toast, but I'm still here.

TUBERCULOSIS TESTING

Tuberculosis bedevils cattle farmers across Britain, and the ways in which it is dealt with are controversial. The impact of routine testing by government-appointed vets is immensely time consuming and stressful, as Graham explains.

'It's always back of your mind.'

We are free at the moment. We are due for a test. Last time – two years ago – caused us a lot of problems. You get a test, you do it and it takes a full day to inject, the same to read. You have an inconclusive or a reactor, then test every two months 'til they are clear. It's alright testing in winter when the cows are housed, but in summer you need a day rounding up before the test. You need a day to test. It's a lot of work by time you gathered them up. And it's upsetting for everyone, everyone gets stressed. Get a few abortions – that makes it worse. If you get these reactors, it's even worse. It affects your closed herd. Cows go back generations, but you can lose some of them. Most cows go back to those Dad bought back from Mold years ago. ●

OVERLEAF: Dairy herd near Longnor, early June. **Photo:** Sheila Hine.

Emma Trueman

Emma is a young cattle farmer on Morridge. She describes what happened after one routine test in 2017. The lump that she describes can be an early indicator of TB and is measured for change by an inspecting vet.

Twelve months ago, we had our annual test and they found one IR (Inconclusive Reactor), so that was retested sixty days later and the lump hadn't changed, so she went as a reactor. At the next test, the vet passed everything, and then on the following Monday Defra [Department for Environment, Food and Rural Affairs] rang and said the vet had read the TB test wrong; he had used the wrong chart, and this animal needed to be shot there and then. She was a pedigree heifer, two and a half years old and had just calved. There isn't a price for that, so they just told me I'd have to suck it up and they'd pay me the commercial killing rate. To us it wasn't a reactor, and to the vet it wasn't a reactor. I managed to get someone to come and value it, and they were due to come here at four o'clock on the Tuesday. They came and the slaughterman was here at half four to kill it.

I didn't get any time to even lodge an appeal. They said she had to be shot in the shed. They wouldn't let me take her out into a pen. At that time, I'd got an old stock bull, so he was not very happy; neither were all the other cattle. We calmed him down, and the next day, the duty vet rung up to say the animal was TB-clear and she shouldn't have gone, which was sickening, absolutely sickening. At that point, they said because she was TB-free when they killed her, they didn't know if they were inclined to pay the compensation! It took just under thirty days for them to pay the money.

I feel absolutely sickened and I can see completely where some farmers come from who refuse a test. There's a couple in this area, I think they've even taken them to court, and I can sympathise with them because I said on that day I didn't want them coming back and testing. A lot of people have got it into their heads that it's just the farmer that it affects, but I've seen vets in tears when they've failed a herd. They don't like doing it, and for them I think it needs to be a better system. ●

Colin Pickford

Colin farms at Rainow near Macclesfield where he took over from his father. His family has farmed in the area over many generations. Like many other farmers, Colin blames the prevalence of TB on badgers.

We've got 250 acres or so on Thornsett. It's all steep hill land. We used to mow about twenty acres of meadows, but now we've got no cows, we don't mow as much. We make it mainly into hay. If the weather's bad when we've mowed it, we make it into big bales and wrap it. But they're mainly hay meadows. It's all permanent pasture. We used to have cattle, but TB has come into the area in the wildlife. Badgers are for me the biggest issue that there is in farming – they're not rare, they're not endangered, they're not scarce and they're ruining my countryside. They've wiped out the wildlife – all the peewits, curlews, skylarks, frogs, hedgehogs, little mice, bees, anything that nests on the floor, they're gone. If you listen outside now, there's no sound, no cuckoos, nothing. Round here, if sheep get stuck on the back, the badgers eat them alive, and I've got pictures of that two years ago – all the vulva eaten off one sheep. We treated her and she went on to have two lambs. But the authorities won't issue these licences to cull badgers. I've had them out here, they've looked, and they say, 'Try putting an electric fence round two fields.' We've got forty-four fields. They do not understand.

Through my young days in the 1960s, we had peewits, curlews, skylarks, snipe, hedgehogs and frogs everywhere. When we used to mow the hay meadows, it was like a bloodbath. Unfortunately, there'd be little frogs and things got chopped up in the mowing machine. But now there's nothing. The badgers have increased in numbers 'til about 2013 when we had about one badger for every five hectares. That'd be one badger for every two fields. The whole area's the same, and they've just killed everything and they're protected – we can't do anything about it. They've just wiped everything out. I haven't seen a peewit chick for about twenty years.

We could see TB creep through the wildlife. It came from Cheshire; it came up to Macclesfield Forest, came up to Torrs on the corner of Kerridge, it came up to Adlington. It was on three sides of us. It slowly crept through, and our cows first went down with TB in 2015. I'd been calving the cows in the spring, and the cows were making good money in the autumn. We were selling calves up to 920 pounds; they came straight off the cows when they looked the best. We had the cows in the shed. They'd have hay all winter and a few brewer's grains when they calved in the spring. When they went down with TB, we had to keep them, and it was costing about thirty pounds a week to corn the calves; and after two tests, we went clear about January. In February, I sold the best calves and they made 700 pounds, which was 200 pounds less than they would have made in the autumn, and it cost me 300 pounds a head to keep 'em. When the government came in, they took a cow off that

David (on left) and Colin Pickford. **Photo**: Christine Gregory.

'They were all home-bred cattle. They've all gone now.'

had got a very young calf on it. It had no mother, so it dragged itself up and it was a scrawny little thing and it only made 400 pounds, and it's still cost me just as much to corn that one. Financially, you can't keep doing that. You have to produce enough fodder for say twenty cows, but if you've got to keep the calves then you've got forty. And if you don't go clear, you've still got them next year because you have to keep them two years to try and fatten them. Then you'd have sixty. The cows keep calving, but if one year you go clear, you'd sell them all and you'd made enough fodder for sixty and you'd only got twenty to feed. You can't make plans like that. So I says, 'They'll have to go.' We had the mothers and the grandmothers. They were all home-bred cattle. We bred them up to just the size of animals we wanted. They'd got good feet, good udders, good confirmation, good temperament. They've all gone now. •

David Pickford

The pain caused by untimely loss of farm animals is often keenly felt and is expressed here by Colin's son David.

We'd built up the perfect herd of cattle for this farm. You could go and like have a cuddle with the cows in the field. When you have a dog attacking your sheep, people say, 'Well, it doesn't really matter because you're only breeding your lambs for killing anyway.' But we know each sheep. Each sheep has its own little personality and they are an extension of our family. We know them all. •

The complex issues around the spread of TB and badgers are beyond the scope of this book, but this topic was mentioned by almost all of the farmers interviewed for *The Land That Made Us*. The cull of Britain's largest indigenous carnivore has been controversial, and government policy is evolving as further evidence is considered. Other ways of tackling the spread of disease such as vaccinating cattle have also been proposed.

Frank Belfield

That's a big issue with farming in the South West Peak. We went thirty-one years and there was hardly any TB in the country anywhere. If there's a problem, we all want to blame something. They blame the badger. Yes, he's got it and he is spreading it, but if we went clear all them years, where did badger have it from? Intensifying the badger population wouldn't help, but there must have been a source of infection for badgers to get so infected to do this damage in the cows. •

THE PRICE OF MILK

All the older farmers interviewed for *The Land That Made Us*, however small their farms, kept cows and sold milk up until the 1970s, which saw the beginning of greater specialisation and expansion of dairying. Since then, the dairy industry has undergone a transformation in input, outputs and technical advances in milking and in the breed of cows, which were until recently predominantly the high-yielding Holstein Friesian (the black and white cows). Now a lot of farmers are cross-breeding their cattle to produce greater longevity and hybrid vigour.

In 2014, the UK produced 14.6 billion litres of milk – the highest annual figure since 1990 – but the number of dairy cows had declined steadily in the intervening period. Fewer cows were producing a greater quantity of milk. Between 1975 and 2014, the average annual milk yield per cow had almost doubled from 3,750 litres to 7,445 litres.

The UK is wedded to its dairy industry. It is our single largest agricultural sector and we still have high levels of milk consumption, but how we buy our milk has changed. Doorstep deliveries are now a rarity and most of us buy our milk at the supermarket. The regulation of the industry has also changed with the demise of the Milk Marketing Board. The big supermarket chains now dominate the fortunes of British farmers. The UK is the third largest milk producer in the EU, after Germany and France, and the tenth largest in the world. Dairy herds have grown, with the average numbers almost four times what they were in the 1970s.

In 2014, the average number of cows per UK herd was 133, compared to 97 in 2004 and 75 in 1996. However, as herd sizes have grown, the number of dairy farmers has declined drastically. In the South West Peak, the Agricultural Census of 2009 showed that since 2000, the number of dairy farms in the area had decreased from 109 to 58 – just 13 per cent of all holdings. The figure had declined to 11 per cent in 2016. This reflects the national picture. Half of Britain's dairy farmers went out of business between 2000 and 2010.

Dairy farmers were in the news in 2012, with images of farmers demonstrating and pouring milk down the drain as the prices they were paid failed to reach production costs. Prices had stalled while feed costs increased massively. In 1997, farmers were receiving twenty-five pence for a litre of milk. In 2015, when we spoke to Alan Dickinson from the NFU, few farmers could get that price. Alan relates an account from a meeting with local farmers in 2015.

'The thing which bothers me is the fact that we are milking 150 cows now, 100 ten years ago and 60 cows twenty-five years ago, just to earn the same profit from them. How many will we have to milk in thirty-five years' time to make it work?'

John Stone, dairy farmer

Alan Dickinson

One farmer was very open about his business accounts. He produces about a million litres so, as he said, 'It's easy numbers to play with.' Compared to what he was getting twelve months ago [2014], the price he'd be getting now [2015] meant 140,000 pounds per year less. Now that's quite scary. He'll admit that the previous year was the best year he'd ever had. But all that investment he was going to do, and that the money was letting him do, he now can't do. The supermarkets keep putting milk on the shelves at a very low price to try and get customers in. It's a loss leader, so they keep saying. Do they really need to keep using milk for this reason? The price paid to farmers for July 2015 was something like 23.2 pence, but now each month it keeps going down. Today, it's probably twenty-one pence and a bit, and there's some only getting teens of pence.

It's also artificially propped up by those on the supermarket contracts (the dedicated supply contracts), where they're still above thirty pence. So you've got some people on over thirty pence and some on under twenty pence for exactly the same product. Tesco have this big headline: 'We pay our dairy farmers a sustainable living so they can pay themselves a wage and money to re-invest.' But there's only a certain percentage of their milk is actually from the dedicated supply contracts. The rest comes from the farmer, who's at a much lower price that just gets chucked in with it. I think twenty-five pence would be a reasonable minimum amount.

The dairies want to keep costs down, so if they can get 20,000 litres from one farm, it costs them less than getting 5,000 litres from four farms. But I would argue the big farms are probably struggling as much as any in some ways, as they also have high costs such as labour and machinery. It's all about which contract you're on. If you're on a good Tesco or Sainsbury's contract, you haven't got any worries.

One of the last remaining farmer co-operatives is First Milk, and they're struggling financially. It's about four pence per litre that First Milk take back off their farmer members. This isn't being invested in the company; it's paying the wages. So if you're only getting perhaps seventeen, eighteen, nineteen pence and they're taking four pence off you, you're left with half as much as the man on the Tesco contract. You've no chance.

Townspeople don't understand when you say, 'I've got to get up every day to milk the cows.' It's 365 days a year. Those cows want milking twice a day every day of the year and it is a major commitment. I'm sure most dairy farmers will agree that when the circumstances are right, they can make very good money, but they've had to earn it and there's a massive amount of investment. Replacement heifers might be costing an average of 1,500 pound a head; that's just the livestock, let alone milking parlours that probably start at about 50,000 up to 150,000 now. If you want a robotic milker, they're about 80,000 or 90,000 each, which only milks sixty cows. There's a lot of costs.

You slog your guts out because you're wanting to pass this down to your next generation. That's the sole reason you do it. It's all about pride. You want to say, 'I've done a great job; here you are, son – have it and carry on the tradition.' Most families do keep going a very long time on the same farm. Big farmers will struggle because large farms have big costs, and families can't run large farms as a rule. You're paying outside labour. If the milk price goes down, the employees still want their wages; you wouldn't expect any different. Whereas you have a family farm, you haven't, as a rule, got the same costs. A lot of the business expenses come out of the farm, which also pay the sons' living expenses and all the rest of it, and you can batten down the hatches and make do. You don't need to keep renewing the machinery; you manage because it's your family; you do without a wage, you live, you don't go hungry, but you don't have a holiday or anything like that. Personally, I think the medium-sized farm will probably keep going the best, as hopefully they can keep their costs under control but still have a good output. ●

THE SOUTH WEST PEAK – PRIORITIES FOR CONSERVATION
Denise Jarman

The lapwings went when they changed it from pasture to when they started silaging. I do worry for the wildlife now with all the intensive farming because you know my children don't have memories like that. Your children, your grandchildren, even if you stay here, will not have memories like that. It's not just the lapwings, though, is it really – it's everything, isn't it? It's the butterflies as well. When will it stop? ●

Conservation bodies have long assessed land-use priorities based on landscape scale ecosystem services. These services are the benefits human society derives from the natural world, which are environmental, economic and cultural. Such services have increasingly underpinned EU and national policy. In the South West Peak, the principal value of uplands for carbon sequestration, water supply, flood control and habitat for endangered species is reflected in funding priorities. For three decades, support to farmers has been targeted towards conserving and repairing landscapes and habitats rather than increasing productivity.

The focus of agri-environmental schemes has, in many instances, been a case of paying farmers to undo the environmental damage they were paid to do in the previous decades. In the 1980s, evidence of the negative impacts of intensive farming led to the first government schemes to encourage wildlife-friendly farming. Environmentally Sensitive Areas (ESAs) were created in 1987.

With them came incentives to conserve, enhance and recreate landscape features and wildlife habitats, and to encourage public access. Countryside Stewardship was introduced in 1991 to increase diversity in the farmed landscape by improving and extending wildlife habitats and conserving archaeological and historic features (such as walls and field barns). These two schemes were superseded by Environmental Stewardship in 2005, which funded farmers and land managers to improve water quality, reduce soil erosion, improve conditions for farmland wildlife, and maintain and enhance landscape character and features. There were two levels of funding: Higher Level Stewardship (HLS) and Entry Level Stewardship (ELS).

Many of these ten-year agreements have expired, to be replaced by New Countryside Stewardship, which came into effect in 2016. Decreased funding, specifically less money available to upland farmers, coupled with a move to complex online communication with Defra, has led to poor take-up of this. The Peak District National Park Authority has also funded a few local agreements. In the South West Peak, these have been for such things as hay-meadow and pasture management, and hedgerow and drystone wall restoration.

In 1992, much of the South West Peak – 83,522 acres (33,800 hectares) – was designated as an ESA in recognition of the area's national importance in terms of landscape, wildlife and historic interest. For nearly thirty years, various EU and government funding for sustainable farming has been an important income stream. The opportunities and effects on farms of agri-environmental schemes are reflected in the accounts that follow. The level of ESA uptake was high in the qualifying area of the South West Peak, and Rob Belfield was one of the first farmers to benefit from this and later stewardship schemes.

'The lapwings went ... when they started silaging.'

Denise Jarman

Lapwing on nest. **Photo**: Christine Gregory.

Rob Belfield

Subsidies have ruled my life. In 1992, we were on EU headage payments. We were keeping as many sheep as we could. And then ESA came out. We went to the first meeting. There was a chap from ADAS,he was desperate to get farmers to sign up.[10] One or two smaller farms round were joining the basic scheme. He came to see us. We were young and upcoming and had got a lot of land for our age. I'm sure he thought if he got us to join, he'd get others to join. He came and we walked all round the Mermaid and he asked, 'Where are you fertilising; where are you spraying?' We only spread two bags over some of it; and he said, 'I can get you about 8,000 pound to carry on as you are, as long as you write everything down.' That was more than I was making; it was a huge boost. He got us signed up. We got lapwings, we got curlews, we got wetland and we got orchids. I don't know what they are – we had yellow flowers, blue flowers. 'Don't fertilise it and don't spray it' – but it was sixty degrees steep, so no one was going to anyway. We spread our nitrogen on the green bits and there was plenty of wildernessy bits that all fell within the rules.

The basic payment on the scheme was 8,000 quid and you'd get 80 per cent on doing up your stone barns. You put your invoices in, ESA paid it. It's all done traditional. We were taking advantage of the scheme, but the scheme was there to be used. I can't count up how many metres of walling we have done. We have had up to eight men at one time

The Belfield family. **Photo**: Sheila Hine.

'They are wanting to put the world back to how it was.'

---

10 Agricultural Development and Advisory Service. In 1992, ADAS became an Executive Agency of MAFF until the business was privatised in 1997.

doing walls. Ever since we got married, we've had tradesmen working on the pig cotes, big barns, stables. We have done 1,500 metres of hedgerows, 3,000 metres of fencing either side. They are wanting to put the world back to how it was.

The 8,000 was taking the pressure off, so we eased back on sheep. We have never eased back on cattle because cows do the ground good. We have had cattle up on the moor-type ground forever, and we still have. Partly because of environmental payments, we have never increased the number of animals. We have gone for bigger animals, better breeds, more mules then Texels. Then when it changed from headage payments to SFP (Single Farm Payment), we went from nearly 1,000 sheep having 1,000 lambs to 700 sheep with 1,000 lambs and better lambs cos we were on Texels and mules. We kept the daughters out of them, and we have gone for more Limousins and Belgian Blue cattle, finishing them, making more money out of them now.

On the right-hand side of Axe Edge, we have 120 acres of semi-moorland classed as SSSI [Site of Special Scientific Interest] moorland. The bloke who had it before covered it with sheep, or had done for quite a while. With it being SSSI, we knew when we bought it you can't spray, you can't fertilise. It's just got to be left to its own devices. In this last ten years, it's gone way back to what it was when we bought it. Rushes are filling up, rough grasses are filling up, bilberries are coming, there are patches of heather coming but not much. It's got everything to do with bogs. It's rough grazing – that's what they want. It's not what I want, but the Higher Level Stewardship pays the mortgage.

Of the 120 acres, I would say there is fifty that you could really up your animals and grow some good grass on because there's some really deep peaty soils. You would still have fifty, sixty, seventy acres of swampy bogs and steep bank sides you can't get at. The animals don't get in 'em – it's too wet, too boggy. They tend to focus on where they can get. This is my argument with a lot of the HLS schemes at the moment. They focus on the entire field, but up here the fields are that big, you have got patches. It doesn't make sense. You've got to graze and manage the whole field, but it doesn't really work. I don't know how you could work it over a big 'one scheme fits all' sort of idea. I'm glad I'm in, for a financial point of view, and I'm not resting on my laurels, but I think we've all been conned now, we're all in the same spot. I think we have even less chance of making a living from the animals. We have the same number of animals spread over a bigger area. ●

WADERS IN THE SOUTH WEST PEAK

The South West Peak, with its upland moors, blanket bog, dry heath, wet pastures and meadows, is important for many bird species, in particular waders that depend on such areas to breed. In spring, curlew and lapwing return from their wintering grounds to raise their young in damp pastures, marshy areas and moorland. The bubbling, tumbling call of the curlew and the distinctive cry of the lapwing (or 'peewit' – a name that imitates its call) are the sounds of returning spring, defining our sense of wild upland spaces. The sound of a snipe's drumming – made by its outer tail feathers while displaying – once heard is never forgotten, and has been described as the bleating of the 'goat of the wind'. All three species are in very serious decline, and most other bird species associated with farmland are also in trouble. The main periods of decline in the South West Peak coincide with the periods of greatest agricultural change, with extensive drainage of marginal land, ploughing up and reseeding of old pastures, use of inorganic fertilisers and destruction of hay meadows.

The South West Peak is still home to nationally important populations of waders. Lapwing, curlew and snipe have held on in the area, but their populations all declined by more than 75 per cent between 1985 and 2009. Long-term population trends in key hotspots show a freefall decline from 1985 of 81 per cent for lapwing, 89 per cent for snipe and 75 per cent for curlew.

Several sites in the South West Peak designated as Sites of Special Scientific Interest (SSSIs) and Special Protection Areas (SPAs) owe the status to their wader populations. Lapwing and curlew are UK priority species, with curlew as top priority in the area. Leek Moors SSSI is important to the national snipe population as it supports one of the most significant southerly populations and maintains the species' UK range.

Britain holds around a quarter of the world's curlew population, a species now listed as 'near threatened' on the IUCN Red List.[11] There are around 68,000 breeding pairs in the UK. Sixty per cent of them are in Scotland – the bulk of the remainder in northern England. Many more come to overwinter on our coasts. The South West Peak curlew population is the most significant southerly upland population in the UK and, as with snipe, is particularly important in terms of the UK range of the species, as it links those further south with the larger upland populations in the north. Many consider the curlew to be Britain's highest-priority bird species for conservation action.

Waders have been included as target features in agri-environment schemes over the years. For several decades, the Peak District National Park Authority has worked with the RSPB and Natural England on the Peak Birds Project and the Wader Recovery Project. Work has included anti-predator fencing aimed at keeping badgers and foxes out; nest cameras have been employed to see at what stage nests or chicks fail; and nest guards stop trampling by grazing animals.

Curlew. **Photo:**Christine Gregory.

---

[11] The International Union for Conservation of Nature's Red List of Threatened Species provides extensive information on the global conservation status of animal and plant species.

Brian Wainwright

Brian remembers the early years of the ESA scheme and work that he and his wife Noreen did to attract lapwing onto Parkhouse Farm, Meerbrook.

We went into the ESA in the early '90s because I'd met my wife Noreen. I thought it was fairly ordinary round here. She pointed out how special it is and what we have got. We went more into the ESA and that kind of farming sensitively for the environment. Also, Noreen wrote about it. We had the lapwing project on the top ground; we did six scrapes for the lapwings and Noreen wrote about that. That was in *The Countryman*, and it was the start of bits and pieces that Noreen wrote about that got us onto Radio 4 *Farming Today*. Rebecca Skidmore came out and interviewed me in some traditional hay meadows. We were in a traditional hay-meadow scheme and we'd got the lapwing project. Some of my fields have never been ploughed and they've got lots of ox-eye daisies and vetchling. You need some of that herbal stuff, all good stuff for your cattle.

We went out of the scheme and didn't bother going back in. I think there was a lot of people dropped out when there was a new type of scheme. It didn't get taken up like they thought it would do. If it's too complicated, farms won't take it on. We were in a Nitrate Vulnerable Zone.[12] We are still on the traditional farmyard manure; we're not on slurry at all.

There isn't a cubicle on the place. It's all housed on straw, no spreading regulations. I believe it's best for the land. We do use a bit of fertiliser, but not much at all. Some years, we don't use any. I don't think there's any disadvantage. It's the most natural thing: rotted bedding muck. I always think what you put on this year, you get back the next. That's how I think it works. I buy six loads of straw for the winter or one load a month. Cows eat some too, and they look well.

I suppose I like to see traditional fields with various flowers, harebells, that kind of thing. Lapwings and skylarks are supposed to have declined, but we have skylarks here just same as always on the top ground. We have got gorse on what we call the Middle Parks. Middle Parks is all gorse – excellent habitat for linnets. I suppose it's not a benefit for the farm, but it is what I like to see – that's why we do it or why we have done it. Wildlife needs all them various types of habitat. I suppose they class deer as vermin, but it's nice to see the deer. I see as many as thirty deer. I suppose there would usually be four or five stags about. ●

---

12 Much of the South West Peak falls within what is called a Nitrate Vulnerable Zone (NVZ). NVZs are (by European Union directive) areas designated as being at risk from agricultural nitrate pollution. They include about 55 per cent of land in England. Farmers with land in NVZs have to follow mandatory rules to tackle nitrate loss from agriculture. (Environment Agency, 2017.)

Upper Dane Valley. **Photo**: Sheila Hine.

Geoff Tunnicliffe

Geoff and Margaret Tunnicliffe keep stock on the Roaches by agreement with Staffordshire Wildlife Trust, in addition to the stock kept at Manor Farm in the Dane Valley. They have experienced numerous problems with the constraints of stewardship agreements, but like all the farmers we spoke to, they have a great love and concern for the wildlife on their land.

We would be struggling without the environmental payments. We wouldn't survive without the Single Farm Payment. We've taken those environmental payments. We shouldn't have done; we should have told them to get stuffed. We want to farm properly, but they've made us do things that we shouldn't be doing.

A lot of the good places are SSSI. That's what gets me about these experts. They find something on your land, whether it be a bird or a flower, and the first thing they tell you is 'We want the gate shutting.' You've probably put your sheep and the cattle on the 1st of May, and they want a patch of land, so we can't put anything on until the middle of July. By the middle of July, the grass has got up, gone rough and this bird (or any ground-nesting birds) and all the plant life will be smothered out. A peewit won't nest in deep grass. It likes bare land.

'We were very keen to preserve the nature and the birds and the animals. You know we're very conscious of conservation and we're up for it and we don't want to overgraze anything.'

Margaret Tunnicliffe

The first thing that they want to do is cut the grazing period down by 50 per cent. That grass will smother the plant, and in ten years' time that plant'll be gone, and it'll be my fault because I'm the farmer. The person who told me'll have gone on somewhere else.

We bought poor land that hadn't been farmed for years. Either the farmer had got old and worn out and didn't farm it particularly well, or in one case the farmer lived down Cheshire and he used to send cattle up here just for the summer. So we bought this land thinking we will improve it. And they come within a very short time and say, 'Oh, we don't want that land improving; we want to cut the grazing down even more.' They talk about a decline in the waders. I don't think there is a big decline. I think they aren't on the sites that they used to be – they've moved on to different fields.

The biggest problem with these schemes is you can only be on a lot of these fields and the moorland for five months. What do you do with them the other seven months? On your own farm, it's bad enough sustaining those animals. But when we took the Roaches over, we'd not only our Manor Farm animals, the Roaches sheep had to come back. For quite a few years, we sent a lot of sheep away into Cheshire in the winter, which helped. But there's not as much of that land now because the Cheshire farmers have gone into this New Zealand method of milk production and a lot of their cattle stay out all year round, so there's no sheep grass. It's made it very, very hard.

My farm, the original farm, gets very overgrazed in the winter because you've got to have those sheep at home because you aren't allowed to out 'em on the moor. Traditionally, you used to bring the sheep down for tupping and then put 'em back on the moor for up to a month before lambing, and then bring them back for lambing. Now once you've bought 'em off end of September, we can't go on again 'til the 1st of April. They don't lamb 'til the 15th of April, so we can't go on 'til the 1st of May. We're struggling, trying to get them [Natural England] to allow us to leave our hoggs on in the winter. We'd have less mither at home, plus the hoggs would get used to being on the hill because they get hefted. In the winter, they would spread out and get used to living in certain parts of the moor, and when you put 'em back, years to come, they remember where they came from and go there.

A private farmer, he bought the Roaches and he put well over a thousand ewes on it. Well, of course it got hammered, and then the Peak Park bought it off him and cut the numbers right down. I think we're only allowed to put 200 on now, on 600 acres. There isn't enough on it to graze the rougher bits, and we also put cattle on it now. We put ten cattle on it.

If it's a farm, it'll always have to be kept green. They want wet boggy land. Well, nothing lives in wet boggy rushy land, only vermin. The birds don't live in rushes this deep – how they going to get in 'em? It's totally ridiculous. They should let you drain the very wet bits and lime 'em, make 'em sweet. And if you've got grass growing there, that takes the moisture out of the land. Grass does, rushes don't; and it'd be better for the bird life and the farmer and everybody, but they can't see that. The best land for wildlife is that land you're allowed to farm properly. These experts, they've all got a different opinion, but some of them have got tunnel vision. They can't see the whole picture. I'd hate for me dad to come back now, to see the fields, the state they're in, some of the pasture land – he'd be totally disgusted.

We're conservationists, but they are interfering with our way of life, and because they're the boss and we take their money – have to take their money – you do as you're told. The worst thing is all this land you can only go on for five months. Well, there's twelve months of the year. That's the killer. Alright, we've got a good view, but you can't make money out of the view.

But the view won't stop like this unless the farmers allowed to farm properly. They think we aren't interested in the bird life and we're going to farm intensively. You can't farm intensively up here; if you farm as hard as you could, you still wouldn't alter the bird population. The problem is to manage it. To manage it for the environment is to farm it. You can't not manage a land and expect it to go any better. •

Agri-environmental subsidies are paid to landowners, and these are not always farmers.

Colin Pickford

When me dad bought Thornsett in 1963, he was the last farmer in Rainow that bought a farm. Since then, every smallholding's been bought up by people from outside, business people, wealthy people. They used to buy the small farms and sell the land off. Now they coming back into what used to be farms. They're buying them and they're buying land back now so they can have land round them that they can control and make sure nobody builds on them. They can say that they're the active farmer and they've got this guaranteed money coming from the Single Farm Payment that's just an investment for them. A serious problem is that these payments aren't rewarding farmers; these payments are going to the landlords. My son David had rented small parcels of land off up to twelve different landlords. He doesn't get a single penny subsidies. It goes to the landlord, which is what they call the 'active farmers'.

We've got one particular businessman in Rainow, he owns nearly half the village. This guy, he was an industrialist. He bought all the land as it came up. He bought a lot of the small farms, did the houses and buildings up, sold them off separately and kept the land. He still owns it all. He employs one man and he ranches it. At lambing time, he'll go round about two or three times a week to look at the sheep. I've seen all my sheep this morning before you came.

The finances aren't good; it's only that my wife works and David's partner works. She's got a good job: she's an accountant. And you know that's just what makes it pay. Over the last ten years, we've averaged about 8,000 pounds a year profit. That's including about 20,000 pounds a year payments from the schemes, so in other words we've been making 12,000 pounds a year loss without that. •

David Pickford

If I go to look to buy a farm, which is something we have done in the past, you go to the bank and you say this is 'my business plan that we've put together'. They normally laugh you out of the bank because you put in the payments that you get and they look at it and when we go out of Europe, them payments might stop so you can't put that in. So you've got no chance. •

Adrian Rochford

Adrian used to work for Natural England as an adviser on the Higher Level Stewardship Scheme. Now he works part-time for Trent Rivers Trust as Tittesworth Catchment Adviser. In both of these roles, Adrian has developed a strong collaborative approach in his work with farmers.

To me, the most important part of an HLS adviser's role is to get a really good understanding of a particular farm and the particular habitats there, then tailoring the land management prescriptions to help maintain or improve these habitats. It is important that the adviser is able to spend time on the farm and engage with the farmer to get to know them well and explain the reason for the management prescriptions – not just tell them what to do from a drop-down menu. I altered the prescriptions, after discussing with local colleagues, and worded them to be more user-friendly to the agreement holders.

In late 2010, due to cuts being required to Defra and its agencies, Natural England had to reduce its staff by 400, mainly by voluntary redundancies. I applied, and was allowed to leave at the end of May 2011. Before I'd even left, I was being headhunted by Trent Rivers Trust. The objective of the TRT role is to work closely with farmers to help them not to pollute the reservoir (and boreholes) with pesticides and organic pollutants like slurry. I try to do this with a light-touch approach, just discussing how best to overcome issues such as slurry or pesticide pollution,

Adrian Rochford doing soil sampling. **Photo**: Sheila Hine.

'If there is no environmental stewardship money coming in, most farmers won't be able to afford to manage the land in an environmentally sensitive way.'

and describing examples of best practice or methods that have been shown to work on other farms and encouraging people to consider them. The results of monthly water sampling, from standard sampling points and additional investigational points, often give an indication of the source of the nutrient and pesticide pollution. I endeavour to pinpoint the origin of pollution and advise on how best to avoid it in the future.[13]

The farmers I work with are principally intensive dairy farmers and they are trying to squeeze productivity out of every square metre of their farms. There are very few areas that they feel they can allow to be valuable habitat. But having said that, there are a handful that have got HLS agreements. Some of those are actually intensive dairy farms and they have got land management options which, for example, might benefit snipe, lapwing and curlew and perhaps some remnants of heathland.

I think that loss of valuable habitat such as moorland into relatively intensive grazing or silage ground had mostly happened several decades ago. In terms of soil damage to the intensively managed grassland,

I would say that most of the switched-on farmers aren't really damaging their land. They know that good structure is important and they realise that it's sensible not to traffic on land when it's soaking wet, and that timing of slurry applications is important. Such understanding has been improved by various events organised by Natural England through Catchment Sensitive Farming and by Trent Rivers Trust through events funded by Severn Trent Water. There are, I am sure, other events organised by other organisations that have helped too, as of course do regulations such as Cross Compliance and various guidance documents.[14]

That doesn't mean to say that there aren't times when the rules go out the window, like in 2012, when the summer was wetter than a typical winter. Tremendous damage was done to soils that summer, but most of the farms have healed pretty well since then. If the farmers feel that they are damaging their land, they are making efforts to change their systems investing in lower-ground-pressure tyres, soil-loosening equipment and umbilical systems (of which there are pros and cons). They are mindful of the need to minimise damage to their soils. I'm not suggesting that

---

13 This advice has led to a 50 per cent reduction in levels of harmful chemicals in the water. (Trent Rivers Trust, 2016.)
14 Cross Compliance is a set of rules which farmers and land managers must follow on their holding if they are claiming rural payment through the Basic Payment Scheme (BPS). They cover public, animal and plant health, environment, climate change and good agricultural condition of land, and animal welfare. (Defra, 2017.)

everything is perfect, because it isn't. But the trouble is that most farmers are under such [financial] pressure to increase stock numbers and maximise output that this puts immense pressure on the soils and the surrounding ecosystems. If only they could be guaranteed a good income for the meat and milk they produce, many farmers would perhaps reduce stock numbers and settle for a less stressful life. Maybe I am not being realistic!

It depends very much on the mindset of the current owner and whether they've got many years ahead of them. There will be some who so strongly believe that it is right to manage the land in an environmentally sensitive way that they will keep doing so with or without Environmental Stewardship support. But if they simply cannot afford to keep on managing the land that way, then valuable habitats could be lost. It's very worrying because if there is no environmental stewardship money coming in, most farmers won't be able to afford to manage the land in an environmentally sensitive way. Some may decide to sell up and rent the land to intensive dairy farmers who will manage it for two or more cuts of silage and tanker thousands of gallons per hectare of slurry onto it. That would be very sad, after so much has been invested into improving the habitat for botanical diversity and wildlife.

The likelihood of uptake of the new schemes, which will replace for example Upland ELS, is negligible because there is no money in it for the farmer, so they can't entertain it. From what people have told me, there is a lot of obligation put on the farmer, and very little in terms of income back for it. It's just a non-starter. Interestingly, in the arable lowlands, the uptake of field margins is, I believe, massive, and a lot of farmers have taken up options such as pollen and nectar mixes on headlands. These are really good for bees, butterflies and birds, and farmers buy into it.

There seems to be a feeling that there is some sort of conspiracy to make the new schemes completely unworkable. If that is the case, it is very short-sighted and tragic. There is a lot of worry and concern amongst many people involved in the environmental sector. •

WHAT IS PRODUCTIVE LAND?
Alan Dickinson of the NFU

The moorland out there, waste of time. You can't keep stock on it; it doesn't carry one sheep per five acres. You want five sheep on one acre. It's bred into you that you must produce and you must improve and you must get better. That's not being intensive, it's just bred into you, into 95 per cent of farmers.

The worry for most farm businesses is how to make a living and yes, it'd be great to do everything flowery and nice, which is how most farmers would ideally have it, but that doesn't as a rule pay the bills. I've got one customer up in the hills who tells me 90 per cent of their income is from farm subsidies and environment schemes. In some ways, you have to ask should they be farming and in business because they can't stand on their own two feet. Ten per cent of their income is from the stock. They're living on handouts like the person on Benefits Britain who is on the dole and getting housing benefit and everything else, but the cattle and sheep should be making enough so that isn't necessary.

In the good old days, there was food on the table, a shirt on your back, coal on the fire and a roof over your head. The farmer's trying to use that slurry so he has to buy less fertiliser, so his grass grows better so he can reduce his costs, or make a bit more money. In industry, he'd be called efficient; but in farming, he's a major pollutant and guilty of running an intensive system.

Around Leek, we have some brilliant farmers and I keep saying to them, 'Why don't you just sell up and go down to Stafford or somewhere where you could be self-sufficient – you'd get all that cow muck, you could put it on the land, you could grow your maize, grow your wholecrop.' But this is home – they don't want to go from here because they love where they live.

There's not enough income from the land, and farmers end up having to do another job, which isn't how it should be. You don't have to be necessarily intensive, but you have to have enough stock to create a living. I've got eighty sheep, I've got 150 lambs, and at the very beginning, I thought, 'If I get seven and a half thousand for those lambs, that'd be alright.' Seven and a half thousand might sound like a fair bit, but if you count up all the expenses, I'll be doing well to just break even. For me, it's an expensive hobby, so I have to support the farm with this job. ●

'It's an expensive hobby, so I have to support the farm with this job.'

John Stone

John and Janet Stone farm at Onecote Grange Farm. They have a large dairy herd and some ground in Higher Level Stewardship.

With better mechanisation and better grasses obtained by ploughing the fields, we became more of a modern farm. I think it is the way forward for younger people, but we have got rid of a lot of wildlife, got rid of a lot of hay meadows, which I now look on as essentials in the farming mosaics around the South West Peak. I can remember mowing the hay meadows in 1985 and seeing partridges flying out of them, and seeing great big swathes of meadow vetchling, tufted vetch and field vetch; and once we ploughed the ground, all those went.

John and Janet Stone. **Photo**: Sheila Hine.

Shorthorn cow on the Roaches, August. **Photo**: Sheila Hine.

We used to have the cuckoo in proliferation around our area; that all went. So I think we are our own worst enemy, but we cannot stand still. We have got to go forward. From there onwards, we became a little bit more building-orientated and we put a silage barn up and went on to three cuts of silage per year.

Since 1992, when we went to this cubicle system and silage system, it coincided with wetter weather, when we found it was impossible to make hay, so it worked out to our advantage, really. We always kept pedigrees registering all the cattle, which we've always done since 1980. I had this idea I wanted to be pure Holstein, and starting off with Pure Imported pedigree Holsteins known as PIs. We have taken numbers up to 150 milked cows and we are averaging about 10,000 litres, similar to the herd of Holstein Friesians we had before. We have a lot more young stock as we use sexed semen, so a lot more heifers.[15]

'Our farm was called the hotspot of the moorlands.'

We have more land, so we are not more intensively stocked than before, but we use more fertiliser to prolong the grazing season as much as we can and make as much silage as possible for a rainy day. That combined with some wholecrop we now grow as part of our HLS [Higher Level Stewardship] scheme. Modern grasses still need feeding to get any prolific growth from them and wouldn't survive as well without fertilisers as the old swards with timothy and cocksfoot in. We have clover in all our swards – we love clover. Without fertiliser, clover does better – it gets out above the grass. It fixes its own nitrogen. I think if you can manage without fertiliser and take stocking down according, clover will do a good job for you.

In HLS, we fenced off the streams and we only graze those areas once or twice a year. There has been a significant increase in flowers, and I absolutely love it and I wouldn't be without it. And I get paid for it. I wouldn't like to think the payments will end. I would still do it without funding, but financially it wouldn't be worth continuing with it. So I think the vast majority wouldn't do it if there was no funding.

We do need these incentives; we need a mosaic, a patchwork of different species of grass and different environmental schemes so they can be joined up. It's no good having one designated area for wildlife.

Four years ago, we started growing wholecrop; that's really done well because our soils are really strong, although we are 1,000 feet and above.

---

15 Sexed semen is used by stock farmers who wish to produce progenies of a desired sex either female or male with about 80 to 90 per cent accuracy. Sex-sorting technology was developed in the US early this century and has been one way to avoid the wasted lives of bull calves born to dairy cows.

We don't spray it. We fertilise it so weed seeds do come into it eventually throughout the summer while it's growing. Fat hen, chickweed and red-leg are the beneficial seeds for ground-nesting birds like skylark, meadow pipit, linnet, goldfinch and other finches. They really love those weed seeds once the crop's been cleared. We only set the corn in the spring. We have to leave it fallow in the winter for those particular species to make wild weed seeds for overwintering birds.

While that crop is growing for three months, ground-nesting birds such as lapwing, curlew, meadow pipit and skylark find a really good use of the wholecrop. They are undisturbed for three months and they are successful with their nests. It has been the number one benefit to the skylark. We must have twenty pairs of skylarks. Meadow pipits have done just as well. In the spring, when we were ploughing, we had four or five pairs of wheatears. We've seen more wheatears now in the summer and definitely got more hares through the wholecrop habitat. Round here, our farm was called the hotspot of the moorlands. Staffordshire Wildlife Trust have ringed fifteen barn owls every year.

We have lots of orchids and those have definitely increased with the areas that have been managed. I am given guidelines on what to do by the Peak Park and Natural England, but I don't always go with the letter of the law. If we do get an area that is heavily populated with grasses and it's got out of control, we mob-graze it. We let big animals in and they

get rid of the briers because they rip them to pieces with their feet. We find mob-grazing opens it up and gets lots of fresh air into the bushes. Our area is a pleasure to look at it in spring, with lots of primroses. I think keeping those areas grazed out reasonably well helps primroses and most of the flowers on our property. Last year, we found marsh valerian that comes out very early in spring, a beautiful flower, and we also found a trailing St John's wort, which is a very small flower like a yellow pimpernel. We have got about 150 species of flowers growing in our valleys, which is a very high density of flowers if you bear in mind they have been there for thousands of years. When they have been grazed off pretty tightly, you don't see them. Now it's managed, you do, and we get lots of orchids. We've got common spotted, also southern marsh orchid; occasionally we see fragrant, but not very often – it depends if you are there at the right time.

Cattle are absolutely vital. Some enthusiasts seem to think keeping cattle away from managed conservation areas so it can grow wild is just the thing. But it doesn't work. Cattle are the basis for encouraging seedlings that come out of the ground. You will have more birds where there are more flowers.

If it continues in its present state, then payments for HLS are better than other schemes. It's a shame they haven't more money to roll out more HLS areas so farmers could take them on board. I don't think the small farms will be viable – they will be hobby farms for those with good salaries. ●

OVERLEAF: Janet Stone bringing in the cows at Onecote Grange Farm. **Photo:** Sheila Hine.

Frank Belfield

Environmentally Sensitive Area payment solved a lot of problems for me because I wasn't very well. I could do with less work, and this was brown-envelope farming by growing what they wanted and keeping less stock. I'd got regular money coming in. You knew even if you didn't rear enough lambs, you'd got some money to pay the bills with and it took the pressure off. And it was turning the clock back a bit. We were almost going back to Granddad's days. We'd stopped buying anything in, and every year we were running numbers down to comply with what they wanted done. Before, it had gradually got better and better and we'd got control of it – we'd done draining and what have you.

Instead of the farm then going on improving, which it had done for many, many years, this time it started to go back, and it's gradually deteriorated ever since with the benefit of these schemes. It keeps less stock, we'll put it that way.

To get it back to where it was, all you need to do is put it under some pressure again and let 'em eat it off bare and throw a bit o' lime on and off you go again. All it's doing now, and it's a good thing for it, it's not spoiling it. It's resting it and letting its own natural nutrients and trace elements develop again so's in the future somebody else can have another go at it and it'll come back again.

It's how you look at a farm. Is it there to produce as much food for Joe Public as you can possibly produce? Is it there just to make a living? Or is it there at the benefit of taxpayers' money so Joe Public can come and look at what he wants to look at? The wildlife has increased twentyfold, I should think, bird-wise and what have you. There are mushrooms here, eighteen varieties, because it's exactly the right height, it's the right soil conditions, and it faces south-west. They've got to have all them three criteria to grow. It's just gone back natural. I should say production-wise in another five year, the farm will be back to where it were when me granddad come here.

I think it's better now, and if most farms in the hilly areas were like that – and there are a lot going that way – the volume of stock would reduce and would be worth more.

If you don't keep the money in the area, you can't keep the people in the area. You need the folk to stay in the area that know how it works. It's no good trying to import people as guardians. Let somebody make theirself a living with it, as long as he isn't ambitious. If he draws his Higher Level Stewardship and his Entry Level Stewardship and he behaves himself and he keeps a reasonable amount of stock without poaching and over grazing, he will have a comfortable living. But he'll not be able to buy no ground up round it or do any serious progression. But is that a bad thing? Without HLS, it's a non-starter. He would have to push it,

and it would mean a lot of inputs – you would have to go down the fertiliser route and you'd be reseeding and use a lot of corn to pull it back up.

Without what they are doing now, one way or another they are going to lose it. Because if folk leave these farms, they will just run to scrub if they aren't grazed and managed a bit. And if somebody wants to come in and go mad with 'em, they will spoil everything that's been saved. If they take subsidies off, they are going to see some drastic changes, one way or the other.

If I'd got to stay here, I would have done more or less what I've done. But I wouldn't have liked to have a hill farm at all if I had me choice. I would have gone where it was flat. ●

'In another five year, the farm will be back to where it were when me granddad come here.'

PREVIOUS SPREAD: Frank Belfield. **Photo**: Sheila Hine.

138

Scarlet Waxcap mushrooms, a grassland species associated with untreated, unpolluted ground. **Photo**: Sheila Hine.

'My job was going around offering grants to plough up, drain and reseed stuff. Easiest job in the world.'

Chris Manby

When I started my career, I worked for the Ministry of Agriculture. It was in the late '70s and early '80s. My job was going around offering grants to plough up, drain and reseed stuff. Easiest job in the world. I mean, I was a bureaucrat, I was college-trained, and you'd get that 'Oh, he learned it in a book' and all that stuff. But I was just going onto eight or nine farms a day checking grant claims worth thousands and thousands of pounds. You were welcomed with open arms, but I was still a 'graduate bureaucrat'. My colleagues today from Natural England are the equivalent to what I was then. But I was giving them something that they wanted, whereas I think the people now are giving them something they don't want. They want the money but people have been brought up in that post-war ethos of production agriculture. I'm not some sort of expert on agricultural economics, but I just can't see the government now saying they want the uplands to produce food as the top priority because globalisation and everything else has changed the picture massively in the last twenty years. •

Simmental cow and calf. **Photo**: Sheila Hine.

PART 5
The future for farming in the South West Peak

New directions in agricultural policy; farming organically; diversifying; finding a niche, 'hobby farmers'; keeping it in the family; the future.

OVERLEAF: Limousin cross cattle near Gib Torr, Quarnford. **Photo**: Sheila Hine.

PART 5: THE FUTURE FOR FARMING IN THE SOUTH WEST PEAK

As it stands at the time of writing, the UK is due to leave the European Union and the future of farming in Britain hangs in the balance. Currently, UK farmers receive three billion pounds a year in subsidies under the Common Agricultural Policy (CAP). Payments are based on land area, and the lion's share of government funding through CAP goes to the wealthiest farmers with the largest holdings. The top 10 per cent of recipients get almost half of the total payments, while the bottom fifth get just 2 per cent. The Agriculture Bill introduced in September 2018 is set to be the biggest shake-up in UK farming since the Second World War. The intention is fairer distribution of public funds and a very different set of priorities from those half a century ago. The system of Direct Payments will be phased out over a seven-year period from 2021. Smaller farms should benefit under new measures to redirect funds away from the richest land holders and to pay for new schemes, research and development.

The government have promised a green Brexit; a post-Brexit farm policy that will 'invest in the environment and take back control for farmers after almost fifty years under EU rules' and 'legislation to deliver a cleaner and healthier environment for future generations'. The intention is that from 2028, 'Environmental Land Management' (ELM) contracts will be introduced to pay farmers to tackle climate change, increase wildlife habitats and improve water, air and soil quality. The Agriculture Bill promises 'public money for public goods'. These proposals have been received with a cautious welcome by wildlife and conservation organisations that fear the loss of decades of EU conservation measures and effective environmental protection. There is considerable alarm from the farming lobby in that the National Farmers' Union wants to see food production and security at the centre of future policy.

Climate change is at the heart of the Agriculture Bill, and farmers in Britain faced the high costs of extreme weather in 2018, a year that saw freezing winter temperatures with the 'Beast from the East'. This was then followed by a long, hot, dry summer with poor harvests and winter feed used to keep stock alive as summer pastures failed. Through the summer of 2018, the landscapes of the South West Peak resembled parts of Africa, and the moorland of the Roaches caught fire.

Farmers face challenges on all sides, with uncertainties over future financial support, tight margins and uncertain weather. They also face a new challenge as public attitudes to farming and patterns of consumption change. More consumers are concerned about climate change and animal welfare, and have cut down on or given up meat and dairy. The findings in an annual report from the supermarket chain Waitrose show that one in eight Britons are now vegetarian or vegan, and over a fifth are flexitarian (which means they eat meat occasionally). The report is based on research among shoppers in all supermarket chains. Food choices now reflect a growing awareness of the environmental impacts of farming animals.

Harvesting wholecrop on the Stones' farm, Onecote, with Andrew Turnock on the chopper. **Photo**: Sheila Hine.

David Dobbin, chairman of Dairy UK, fears a 'demographic time bomb' as young people increasingly shun milk. High input costs and low prices dominated by supermarkets have already driven many farmers out of dairy. Half of the nation's dairy farms went between 2006 and 2016. Industry analysts believe there will be fewer than 5,000 left by 2026.

The Waitrose findings came at the same time that the World Wide Fund for Nature (WWF) published a stark report showing that globally through climate change, habitat loss, overexploitation and agriculture 'we've killed 60 per cent of wildlife on earth since we walked on the moon'. Debbie Tripley from WWF has said, 'The UK has some of the most degraded nature in the world … If the UK wants to be a global leader on the environment, we have to walk the talk here at home. That means making a long-term investment in this transformation.'

Farming is at the heart of this transformation, and the following accounts reflect the numerous ways in which farmers are tackling their future in the South West Peak. They are the next generation of dairy and beef farmers, specialist breeders, smallholders and diversifiers.

THE SPECIALIST SHEEP BREEDER
Neil Richardson

Neil has spent thirty years farming at Big Fernyford Farm, Reapsmoor, between Longnor and Warslow. From 1968, Big Fernyford was farmed by Sylvia and Michael Woolley (see page 88). Neil is a former champion sheep shearer and, with his partner Dorota and youngest son, is now a specialist sheep breeder.

I should have stuck to football, but I was hooked on sheep. I started working for a farmer when I was nine. I got a couple of sheep when I was eleven, and then carried on working for him 'til I was fifteen. Then I went self-employed and I had about thirty sheep of my own and was helping one or two farmers. When I was nineteen, I started catching sheep and wrapping wool for a couple of shearers, and I thought shearing looked easier. So they said, 'You should go to New Zealand and learn to shear.' So I went to New Zealand and spent six months there learning to shear sheep. Then I represented England shearing sheep, and was in the top three for about seven years and travelled all over. I won quite a few competitions.

'It's no good breeding something too old-fashioned.'

Young Swaledale ram at Fernyford Farm. **Photo**: Sheila Hine.

I applied for about ten or twelve different farms with North West Water, the National Trust, Sheffield Corporation, Haddon Estates – all sorts of farms. Any farms that came up, I applied for, but they all said 'you've not got enough money or experience', and then this one came up. I think out of seventy applicants, we were fortunate or unfortunate enough to get the tenancy. That was in 1988, and we've been trying to straighten it out and maintain it ever since. It's partly owned by Natural England and partly by the Peak District National Park. It's cost a lot of time, a lot of money and a lot of effort, and there's still plenty to do. I think we've done a really good job for them.

Twenty-one years ago, we got into Swaledales because I used to spend a lot of time shearing sheep in the Yorkshire Dales where they all kept Swaledales. We got into breeding them and we've done quite well ever since, really. It's not just me and my partner Dorota, but my son now as well that's in the Swaledale world. He's thirteen, and he got champion at Hawes last year, which is something that some of those Yorkshire boys have been trying to do for all their life. He's dedicated to Swaledale sheep, and hopefully he'll carry on and breed some more champions. He certainly knows what's a good Swaledale and what's a bad one.

We've been breeding for a few years what they call snod-woolled sheep. This is shorter wool, because the Swale goes on to produce the mule, and the mule breeders are wanting shorter, tighter wool to get their lambs looking tighter and more meaty than the shaggy-woolled ones. So I don't think any of the top breeders that are breeding pure Swaledales are keeping woolly ones. They're all going for the snodder wool.

We've had success with quite a few rams that we've sold for twelve, fifteen, twenty thousand. I don't think we'd get them sort of prices for shaggy-wool ones. And now we're hooked on breeding rams. With the Swales, it's all cosmetic. Before, they used to have black knees, and now they don't want black knees. They want them fully white down the front and fully black down the back of the legs. Same with the white on the eye. They want a nice big silver eye. Before, it used to be just a stripe above the eye and black below it, and soon it may revert back a bit. We've got to breed a type that will sell. It's no good breeding something too old-fashioned. You've always got the chance with some good bred sheep of getting one to make twenty, thirty, fifty thousand. But with the old-fashioned one, you're never going to get above two or three thousand, so I can't see much interest in that. And I wouldn't want to just breed commercial fat lambs. I'd find it a bit too boring, really. You want something with a bit of interest, so that's the way we're going.

Barney and Neil Richardson, 2017. **Photo**: Sheila Hine.

We've about 200 pure Swaledale ewes, and then we've got 150 Swale hoggs from last year out of those ewes. We have a fairly high lambing percentage for Swales. Last year, we were over 200 per cent on lambing with the Swale. This year, we're about 195 per cent, which helps, but we'd like to get it a lot lower. We would prefer honestly to have 200 singles than have all these twins and triplets. Two hundred fit singles are half as much work because singles don't take much looking after. They've all had enough colostrum and they've had enough antibodies, so they don't get the problems.

We've just sold three or four Swiss Valais ewes for 3,000 each, and they're hardy weather-wise but they're soon susceptible to worms and fluke and foot rot in this wet land. We've had them nearly three years. They've got big heads and they look quite interesting sheep. They're good mothers. They're easy lambing, the lambs grow fast. They're big, heavy sheep.

The farm had a real tight restriction on grazing through most of the year. Natural England said if we had traditional cattle we could graze all year round, and graze the moorlands as well. So we went into Belted Galloways, and in 2004, we got rid of most of the continentals straight away and dwindled the others out. We've never looked back, really. We've only got pure Belted cattle now; they're all pedigree. We've sold quite a few bulls off at two or three thousand each, and we sold a lot of heifers off last year. The Belted Galloways are not a high-priced animal in a market, but we've built our own meat-processing room and we do one Belted Galloway bullock or badly striped heifer about once every six weeks. We sell to neighbours, friends and people we deal with. It's been quite a good venture, really. Most of the butchers that I know are driving round in a Mercedes because they make more for having a beast for a week than we do for having a beast for two years in calving and then rearing it up for beef. But the pedigree stock and the breeding animals are the most important thing, so anything that goes for meat is less important.

My youngest son is only thirteen, but he's desperate to come home and take over. He comes home every night and tells me what I should have done and what he's going to do. He was up early this morning, as he is most mornings. He's up and fed quite a few of the sheep before I got up this morning. He's got some good ideas, and with having his ram make a lot of money last year, he thinks he's God's gift to Swaledale sheep.

We've got plenty of snipe and we've got a couple of pairs of curlews nesting on the farm. This is the first year we've had no lapwing because we're too overrun with predators. The farm originally was famous for the black grouse. It was the largest flock of black grouse in the south of England in the field next to the house. It still upsets us that we've no black grouse here because they were amazing. They were here 365 days, every morning, on their mating arena, the lek site. I think the most I saw was about twelve black grouse cocks and then half a dozen females.

The black grouse cocks were well proud of themselves and would come and lek every morning and we'd actually get one or two in the garden here feeding on the berries. They were brilliant to see.

I think we could probably manage without subsidies. You'd have to tighten your belt, and I think a lot of farms should tighten their belts and just stop relying on the subsidies and do the work. Pay should be for specific environmental projects, rather than paying a blanket payment, because some farmers are doing environmental work and some are just taking the money and doing nothing at all.

It can be an absolutely lovely job working on the farm every day. It's a beautiful location and we're not really living in the real world because we're sheltered down a long driveway. Nature is fantastic. The birds are fantastic. The black grouse were amazing and the lapwings were too, but there's just too many people. ●

In 2018, the Richardson family's young home-bred bull Fernyford Brutus was judged Best Male in the Midlands Belted Galloway Herd Competition. They also won the Best Herd title and went on to win the national title.

THE DIVERSIFIERS
Karen Ballington

Roy Critchlow and Karen Ballington farm at Heathylee House Farm near Hollinsclough. This is a 200-acre hill farm at 1,200 feet to 1,500 feet above sea level. They have a menagerie of animals that include miniature donkeys, guanaco (the wild ancestor of today's llamas), and rare breeds of cattle, goats and pigs. Roy has farmed in the area all his life, while Karen previously worked in the army as a telecoms engineer.

Roy took on a little bit of rough ground up here off his family when he was about fourteen, and started messing about. There wasn't a fence or wall that would hold any animals. There weren't any buildings, so over the years he's worked away to make the money to put the sheds up, and everything he's had to do himself. He used to do farming work, contracting work, wagon driving, anything that's needed up in these hills. I'm originally from Bakewell, so when I retired, I bought a building in Longnor and was renovating it and I started a cafe downstairs, and Roy came in and then started supplying me with eggs. That's how I met him fifteen years ago, and after a couple of years, I found myself in slavery on the farm full-time, grubbing about looking after the animals and living in a caravan. I don't know how that happened. Roy never even had a kettle at the farm when I met him. He used to just come up, work all day, then go home. In the time I've met him, we've managed to put another new shed up and built the house.

He had a great ruck of Warrens [a breed of hens], which was his laying flock, so he always had eggs and a lot of beef cattle. First of all, it was animals to tempt me to come. I said I'd always fancied some alpacas. Well, he went and bought a male guanaco. It wasn't an alpaca, it was a guanaco, and then it was, 'You haven't been to see your animal today.' This is how it started. Of course, then you get tied into it, don't you? I said, 'You've got all these eggs laying about, why not sell some of these hens?' This was before hen-keeping was very popular. Well, he advertised them and they were gone within two weeks, so then we got some more and sold them. We don't do eggs now; we do chickens – but we were one of the first and I'd say for a couple of years that was a very, very good business.

It is wet ground with a lot of rushes. I'd say you were wasting your time thinking you were farming it. You're just surviving and same with the stock. Our stock is hardy, and when we've sold calves and they've gone anywhere from here, you always get the feedback a few weeks later, 'By, them cattle have grown; tell me when you're selling some more.' Because folk appreciate that they've come from an environment like this. Anywhere else you put them is going to be easy on them, so cattle are going to grow better.

Roy likes buying things, and that's how we ended up with the rare breeds. Roy's granddad from down Hollinsclough was famous for British White cattle. So, not knowing cow breeds, I bought him a cow for Christmas, a pedigree.

Karen Ballington. **Photo**: Sheila Hine.

But I bought a White Park with the horns. The British Whites are the polled ones, but they look the same, with little black ears. This is how we ended up in White Park cattle. Roy likes to keep building up, so now he's got a herd of pedigree White Park cattle and he's still running his commercial suckler herd which is all Limousin-bred to old fashioned Herefords and some of his British White genetics.

We're that busy with our nose to the grindstone so that marketing, which is the bit where you make your money, we're not good at. Roy once had a phone call asking if we could supply this restaurant with White Park beef. He says, 'Oh no, I'm not interested. I cannot fatten 'em.' It was Claridge's that were on the telephone. Roy didn't know who Claridge's was. Never heard of them.

'We do all of the business on the internet.'

We used to make the money out of breeding stock to cater to smallholders that wanted two or three for fattening for their own meat scheme. We used to breed Middle White pigs, and we did quite well with them as a rare breed. They're quite a nice friendly little breed. We sell a few of the Jacob sheep to smallholders. They're a popular, pretty-looking breed, and most smallholders want something a bit different, don't they? Ordinary sheep aren't very exciting. People also go mad for pygmy goats. We supply a lot of things to smallholders. But you're dealing with people that aren't experienced with stock, so you do have to be very responsible with what you're selling them and the advice you're giving them. You add a bit extra on because of the phone ringing at ten o'clock at night.

The donkeys are really pets. However, they've earned their keep for the rest of their lives. Roy was having a run of bad luck, and his mum and dad swore that donkeys changed their luck. At the time, we were doing some business with zoos buying guanacos, and a zoo phoned us up and said, 'Do you want these donkeys?' So we bought them unseen and they turned out to be Mediterranean miniatures. One of them must have been one of the first imports into this country from America. She's in retirement now. Two of them were pregnant and one was a jack. They were very sought-after at the time, but we kept them. The donkeys are a success; we've got ten on the farm at the moment. We've a little jack could trade for a thousand to one and half thousand. If we had a little girl, it could be two and half to three thousand pounds. Now you weigh that up against cattle and sheep. But they are pets first and foremost. The donkeys are the most pampered animals on the farm. It's not just the value; Roy's got this thing that donkeys are good luck. You never do donkeys a bad turn.

We had got nearly fifty guanaco at one stage. It's a fibre business and we've sheared them and I've sold fibre. I had some shawls made up and I have managed to sell them as far afield as Japan, America, Edinburgh and London.

I think when a small hill farm sends something to Japan, and they order again, you know you've got something special. But again, it's all down to marketing. The guanacos don't like the rain, but they love the hillsides and they don't mind that the grass is rough. They're not suited to lush grass; they come from remote hillsides.

We do all of the business on the internet. I think if we end up taking anything to a market, you lose money on it. If you manage to sell it over the internet direct, then you stand to make a profit. But things like cattle and your ordinary stock – stuff that goes into the food chain – that hasn't made the leap to the internet yet. You're still forced down the market route unless you've got your own private buyers.

I've been doing ginger beer plants for about ten years now. I started making them for folk in the pub and then I stuck them on eBay. Now I send ginger beer plants all over the world. Daft as it sounds, it used to bring in enough to pay the mortgage over there every month.

We've got SSSI ground up on the tops because it attracts all these lapwings. We have a wealth of bird life on there. They come to our ground, but they don't go to the field next door. Natural England should be looking at what Roy's doing to attract those birds instead of telling Roy how to farm it. If he's been here thirty years farming that ground, they should be saying, 'Roy, what are you doing that nobody else is doing?' Well, that's not how it works out, so they came at us and said 'You must do this, you must do that',

and it restricted the way we could farm. The ground was deteriorating over the course of the ten years and we couldn't make a living, and the money we were getting wasn't covering the shortfall, so we've had to come out the scheme. The farm has deteriorated and the numbers of livestock that we can keep on it, so we had to come up with something else. I said to Roy we could farm people. We don't want them here all the time. We can come up with activities for the day – they get to enjoy the countryside, appreciate the beauty of the area and bring much-needed funds in that support our farming activities for the rest of the year. So we came up with Bog Commander.[16] One thing we have got is terrain for that. We've got mud in abundance. So we looked at that and thought, 'Yeah, we'll go for it.' We can't keep it viable just by farming, can we?

You see people moving in, buying these little smallholdings. They've got great ideas. They're good at the marketing, good at the niche, but they've no idea about how to actually farm the land; what they should be doing to keep it how it should be. You've got to have some of the old folk and you've got to spend a lifetime on a piece of ground to understand it and know what it needs.

There's no point looking back, is there? You've thrown your lot in and yes, it's not easy. We'll never have any money, we're always skint and always worry about the bills. We manage to get them paid eventually, but you always worry, don't you? But I'm here now. I guess it's in your blood after a while; it's certainly under your fingernails. ●

---

16 This way of exploiting a landscape is an unusual approach to diversification, with a Commando-type training course with cargo nets, slides, mud crawls and real bogs.

THE HOBBY FARMERS
David Bullock

David's smallholding is in Sutton, near Macclesfield.

When I was buying it, it was forty acres. It always amazes me that anybody could make a living out of forty acres, but they did, didn't they? They milked cows and they didn't have continental holidays. The day at the auction was their day out, and perhaps an agricultural show now and then was their annual holiday almost.

I decided I couldn't really handle a herd of cows on my own. They were out all the time, but if you had to have the vet or the ministry wanted to check anything, you had to get them in, and you can't do that on your own, even with a bucket of corn. So you're stuck with yourself in the end, aren't you? I decided it was getting too stressful and I couldn't really cope, so I decided to sell the cattle. I sold two meadows to a neighbour. The first thing he did was plough them all up and reseed and re-drain them as well – sad.

The patch I now own, which is twenty-five acres, Natural England describe as 'semi-natural', because it's all had something done to it. I'm not sure if they reseeded it, but they certainly fertilised it, and it's got very few wild flowers in it. It will take a long, long time to recover. I'm untypical because my livelihood depends very little on any income from the land, so I'm able to treat it in a wildlife-friendly manner, but I can understand that those

David Bullock. **Photo**: Sheila Hine.

whose livelihoods depend on it have a different outlook. They have changed the subsidies so that meant that people could be less intensive in their stocking of the land. But I think old habits die hard, don't they?

I've got a couple of flowers that I found are quite rare: ivy-leaved crowfoot and meadow saxifrage. You're talking about a patch of each, less than the size of this room, but it's the actual diversity and the spread of it, isn't it? There are patches of quite wet areas. There's a mix. It starts as acid grassland at the top of the hill and becomes neutral when it gets to the bottom. So that's the difference within just the same holding. You can see that in the plants, that there's more acid up the top. Mountain pansy is right at the top – that only grows over about 1,000 foot and there's a lot of that up there, which is very good.

I've always been an organic gardener, so I've always taken that interest. With a name like Bullock, there must be some agricultural background somewhere. Even as a child, I always fancied being a farmer. But my father's view of that was it was a waste of education to be a farmer. In any case, I never in my wildest dreams thought I could own a farm of any size because they are so expensive to buy into. Normally you inherit them and that's how you become a farmer.

As part of the Higher Level Stewardship scheme, I've done a lot of drystone walling, hedge-laying, had a pond dug and a bit of stone-faced hedge bank. I got most of that done with a bit of financial help. And to please Natural England, I cut down half of the gorse. The gorse is probably a hectare all together. I cut half of it down and got paid 250 pounds for all that; it took me five years. It's not for the money; it was murder. In fact, the worse thing is not the gorse; it's the brambles. In order to ensure that the protection lasts on what I have got left, I have left the land in my will, all except one field, to the Cheshire Wildlife Trust, so that they will be responsible for managing it. ●

'I never in my wildest dreams thought I could own a farm.'

Claire Wolstencroft

Claire and her husband Graham moved into Lane Head Farm near Longnor in 2006. They farmed their smallholding under Higher Level Stewardship – an agreement which ended in 2019. As part of this agreement, Claire has worked with parties of schoolchildren, helping them to build a connection to and an understanding of the countryside. Claire first spoke to us in 2015.

We lived at Macclesfield, but we were cavers and climbers, and we'd wanted to move out closer to the Peak District for a long time. So we drove down the lane and we just pulled up and I said, 'Don't care what it's like inside. I want to live here.' It's the place, the views, the remoteness. The fact that when I got out of the car we couldn't hear any traffic. It was the unspoiltness. The feeling that it hadn't been invaded by the BBC workers and Waitrose brigade. We loved the combination of soft hills, drystone walls, trees, the moors on the top, the sense that it was fairly isolated. The views move up to a bleaker landscape. You can see the changes in it as you look out. I want to live here because I want that view when I wash up. It just feels absolutely right.

Claire Wolstencroft. **Photo**: Christine Gregory.

We moved in and all of a sudden we had fourteen acres and I went 'Oh my God!' My husband's uncle was a farmer, but a farmer in Kent. It was arable farming, so a little bit different, but he does know how to do things like drive tractors and move implements, which was helpful. We've got fourteen acres. What are we going to do? Someone said, 'You can rent it out to a local farmer.' I thought, but I don't know the local farmers yet and we could rent it out to the wrong person and I want to feel that I control the land myself. So I thought we'd better learn what to do quickly. I bought some haymaking machinery without telling Graham, and I bought two cows one night when I was slightly tipsy in the local pub from one of the local wheeler-dealers. Graham came home and went, 'What are them in the field? Where've they come from?' I said, 'Cows. I bought them.' They weren't milk cows; they were beef cows we bought. I did think we might have a house cow and they were Dexters, which you could use as a dual purpose, little ones. So I thought I might be able to handle little ones, but I discovered little ones have vile tempers.

'Sadly, it is the smallholders giving up on stewardship.'

I talked to local people; pretended I knew what I was talking about and then suddenly thought, 'Oh my God, the grass is growing. We're going to have to make hay. We'll have to mow it and dry it.' So we've got this machinery, but how do you use it? With a little bit of help from my neighbour, we sorted out how to fix the mower up properly. We watched a local farmer mow, so we thought, 'Must be a good day for mowing, so let's mow it.' Then we watched him ted it and thought, 'Right, get the tedder out. Let's ted it.' And we copied everything he did, we just copied him.

That was ten years ago. Yeah, it was a very steep learning curve. It was quite good fun and very satisfying when we'd got all the hay in and actually managed to make fairly reasonable hay and do everything without killing ourselves or breaking anything. Got people to help us, and it was quite good. It came with quite a lot of agricultural buildings, so yeah, we had to use them, didn't we?

Because we'd got cows and because we'd got a tractor and because we were making our own hay, we moved in in January, and by end of June, we were making hay. They all assumed that we must have been a farming family. It was about four years on when a local farmer said, 'Someone tells me that you weren't always farmers.' I found people incredibly friendly, incredibly helpful, incredibly welcoming; and I would say our closest friends now, and some of the closest friends we've ever had, are local farmers who've lived here for a long time.

I've actually got a share-farming agreement with a young lad, because two years ago Graham and I both hurt our backs within a few months of each other and we had a very poorly cow. We had to milk her every day and neither of us could physically do it. We had to get one of the local farmers to come down and strip her out every day because we physically couldn't. And I suddenly thought, we're only smallholders, it's not important to us. We've got the cows because we're doing conservation grazing. We've got them because we're caring for the landscape. But actually, if we're having to involve other people and put pressure on them, it's not fair. So we sold the cows and we asked Matthew, who is the son of one of the local farmers, if he would like to share-farm the land with us. So I do the stewardship and conservation, I do educational access. I have groups of schoolchildren coming round for visits. And I trained as a Forest Schools practitioner as well to enhance that because one of my big interests has always been trees, flowers and the environment.

Matthew grazes it with sheep, but between us we discuss which field needs to be grazed, and we're trying to manage it so that the sheep aren't wrecking the flowers that we've already got. He operates within our stewardship agreement and it works really well. I've got a few of my own sheep running with his sheep. He does most of the animal side, I do most of the people side and the conservation side, and between us it works. I've got a few Shetland sheep and Matthew's got about forty-odd.

The stewardship we're on is a ten-year agreement. I've got until February 2019. Without that, we would've just rented it out to a local dairy farmer and he would've managed it how he manages everything else. And that I find sort of sad. Some of the fields round about have got bigger because the walls have gone and the trees along the walls have gone. When your profits are cut, your milk price is going down and down, you don't want to fanny about not being able to mow up next to your walls. You want to just be able to get in your fields and mow it. I understand why the farmers have done it and I understand that your profits are pushed in every corner.

I know some of the larger local farms have areas that are under stewardship. But I don't think many of them put their whole farms under stewardship. It will be a small corner that actually isn't useful for much else. It's people who are on smallholdings and people who aren't dependent on farming for their main income that are the ones that have the luxury of being able to concentrate on conservation. Because around here it's not a rich farming area. You know they're not rolling in it. You don't have time to build or repair drystone walls that you don't need. If you've got a large herd of cattle, it's easier to take the wall out, plough it up and manage it for silage.

If you talk to the lad that's tedding our field at the moment, he would say that you don't make enough from the stewardship. It's supposed to compensate you but actually you just want to put muck on, get the grass growing, get the grass in. The reality is, you need to make life easier for yourself and make it easier to make a profit. You don't want to make it harder. Government is supposedly behind encouraging small businesses, but it certainly doesn't encourage small-scale farming. The way it's set up in this country now, it's encouraging large-scale farming because it is only large-scale farming that's going to be profitable.

I know quite a few who've got corners of land in High Level Stewardship, and I know quite a few of them who say when the agreement finishes, 'We're not going to do it again.' The goalposts change. We've been here for ten years and since we've been farming or, as the local farmers say, 'hobby farming', the paperwork, the regulations change every year. And you do not have time to read every bit of paper. Actually, it's not paper that comes now, it's PDFs. When I look round, some of the most beautiful farms are managed by farmers that aren't in stewardship anyway. They've done it that way for hundreds of years and they aren't going to read the PDFs online.

It's bureaucracy gone totally insane. It's a lack of the wholeness. It's people not seeing the whole story. Somebody not so far from here has just said, 'I will never do stewardship again and I am not even claiming Single Farm Payment because I don't want to be beholden to the government.' I don't think they have yet realised that whether you claim Single Farm Payment or not, you have some legal obligations to keep certain records, and it is not dependent on Single Farm Payment. So what happens when you're not taking a Single Farm Payment? People are thinking if I don't take my Single Farm Payment – especially smallholders with a small amount of land – I don't have to obey the rules. Actually, you still have to obey the rules, but I'm not quite sure what stick they're going to beat you with.

South West Peak, I think, statistically has one of the highest levels of smallholdings in the Peak District certainly, if not in the UK. The farms here, even what we would consider a large farm, would be considered as a smallholding in most other places in the country.

I think there have been too many changes and too much paperwork too quickly. You get used to one thing and it all changes. I know from conversations in the pub that I am not the only person that feels like that and I hear, 'I am not going to do stewardship again.' I think we're going to get less hay meadows because I know that when we come out of stewardship, my hay meadows will go and it will upset me.

I will probably keep one, and I will insist that whoever rents my land leaves that one as a hay meadow because it is really rich in flowers now. But the other ones will just get managed along with the rest of their farm. They will get muck on and they will get mown whenever.

I know one hay meadow that's about to go. I walked through it the other day and I thought, 'This is absolutely gorgeous', but they have come out of the stewardship and the owner said, 'That's it. Now we can mow it whenever we like and we can put as much muck on it as we like'. And you think, that's going to go. It's going to go, and I know my hay meadow up there won't, but I doubt I'll be claiming any payment on it because I'm not going through all the hassle.

My management scheme would be to mow randomly because that's what people always did. Worked with the weather, and it worked. That's how you created the hay meadows. They didn't go, 'Well, we can't mow until the 15th of July.'

Farmers round here are aware there are ground-nesting birds and they've got beautiful meadows and they will leave the area around nests. Most people who've got the sort of land where you're going to get ground-nesting birds tend to have little tackle and smaller trailers. People who keep the meadows as traditional hay meadows are the sort of people who notice the wildlife; whereas people who've got rye-grass monoculture and big tackle don't have the ground-nesting birds, cos the birds don't want to live in those fields.

The younger lads that I hear want bigger, faster, better. I've had the Young Farmers round and walked through the hay meadows and had one young lad say, 'I never even thought of it like that.' I said, 'You know you have the flowers and you have pollinators,' and I said 'Without these flowers, we won't have these species, and they are a really important part of the food chain and the soil cycle, because you need certain microbes in the soil for things to grow really well, and that's something that you're losing as well. And you don't see what's going on under the ground.' And he said, 'We didn't know.' When you're eighteen, do you listen to stuff like that in college? Did you? Cos I didn't. I think now you're going to lose it cos that isn't what farming's about. They're gonna listen to the how to fix my tractor, how to grow more, go faster.

As soon as my stewardship comes to the end, Matthew will just operate on a grazing licence and it'll be his land to do with what he likes. However much I try and persuade him that hay meadows are good, he's not having it. A neighbour has just said, 'We're going to do what we like with the land; we cannot cope with the bureaucracy anymore. I am not prepared to fill in the forms.' These are very intelligent people. Sadly, it is people like us, it is the smallholders giving up on stewardship.

Claire spoke to us again in 2018.

We're just letting the land now and don't have any livestock of our own, and I'm really looking forward to coming out of stewardship because we will manage our field differently. We'll still manage our field for conservation but we won't hidebound by regulations that seem to be the same for the whole of the country, whether you're in Lincoln, West Sussex or Northumberland.

A lot of people started their stewardship agreements ten years ago, and a lot of us had the same experience that actually, rather than ending up with meadow full of beautiful flowers, we've ended up with a meadow full of docks and thistles. We're not allowed to mow until the 15th of July. There's a couple of old farmers across the road and they'll mow in the middle of June. Their meadows are flower-rich and there's hardly any weeds anywhere. We have less flowers now by mowing later. We've been here for twelve years, and talking to a Natural England officer, he's agreed that they have learned over the last ten years of stewardship. So it will be nice to see what happens when we think it's right to mow the meadows, which is what they used to do. To see whether we get more flowers. I think we will. ●

KEEPING IT IN THE FAMILY
Andrew Stone

Andrew grew up on Onecote Grange Farm, the dairy farm run by his parents, John and Janet Stone.

I work as a nutritionist and I go round and see a lot of farms. I work over into Cheshire, the Staffordshire Moorlands and into Derbyshire. I probably see a more diverse range of farms than most people do. I do a lot on the organic side of things, that sends me further downcountry to Chepstow and into the Cotswolds. So I see both sides of things, conventional and organic. I see other ideas and things that could help us here in the South West Peak, but every farm is different, so you can't always take the ideas to another farm. It's probably a hard thing to say, but the smaller traditional farms will end up dying out as the larger, specialised farms get bigger. That's what's in danger of happening because we're competing in a world market with world-market prices which smaller farms can't manage as easily.

More agri-environment schemes would probably help, but they don't really fulfil what you lose in productivity of the land. I've got a scheme on my little bit of land that I bought when I was twenty-eight, and I probably wouldn't have had it if it wasn't for the incentive of the money because I needed it to help pay my farm off. It's given it some kind of income while I was getting the sheds built and concreting the yards and getting it set up for having some cattle across there. Since I've been doing it, I do see the benefits of it. I do like seeing the diversity of the flowers in the

Andrew Stone. **Photo:** Sheila Hine.

'It isn't attractive when you see your parents struggle for forty years trying to make ends meet.'

meadows and it does give me more of an interest in what's around me in terms of natural environment. It's not all about intensive farming systems. It is also about the landscape and the wildlife that lives within it and being part of that balance. It's a shame the way things are going is that these things are going to be lost. You can't expect the people who look after the countryside to not move with the times, because they've got a business to run. Without farming, the countryside wouldn't look like it does anyway.

You need to make a living to be able to stay on the land and keep the skills. It isn't attractive when you see your parents struggle for forty years trying to make ends meet, trying to do the right thing and actually not get that well rewarded for it. It does put people off.

I am confident about my future in farming, but if we were a smaller farm, I probably wouldn't be. I would look further afield or try and buy somewhere bigger. But the price of land, if you look at it from a business point of view, is out of kilter with making a living. So that's got to be corrected somewhere, but I don't know how. ●

Peter Slack. **Photo**: Sheila Hine.

'The two lads are really,
I suppose, running the farm,
which has its ups
and downs.'

Peter Slack

Peter is the son of Arthur Slack, who featured in Part 1. Peter farms with his wife Sylvia and two sons Sam and Matthew at Overton Farm at Taxal above the Goyt Valley. As well as farming, he makes a supplementary living as an after-dinner speaker.

The two lads are really, I suppose, running the farm, which has its ups and downs. They spend money like it's going out of fashion and want everything yesterday, which with a volatile milk price isn't always achievable. But we tend to let them get on with it as much as we dare. They do most things brilliantly, but sometimes make odd mistakes. You don't have to get excited about it – that's life.

Farming has changed a lot. When I was farming with Father, the best days of the year were turning the cows out in spring and finishing haymaking. Now it's passing your TB test and the Single Farm Payment landing on the mat, which at times when the milk price is volatile does help pay some bills. •

Sylvia Slack. **Photo**: Sheila Hine.

Sam and Matthew Slack. **Photo**: Sheila Hine.

'There is a lot of negativity about dairy farming in the press and on social media.'

Sam Slack

Sam Slack

Public perception of farming is a hard one. You're trying to do the best for your cows and everyone thinks you're doing the opposite. Public support is a big one. Milk price, feed price and chasing it. If the milk price goes up, everything goes up with it. And of course, the weather. We have a lot of footpaths and lots of people and lots of dogs. We suffer with neospora, which is spread by dogs and foxes. We've got about 10 per cent of the herd with it and out of the cows that have got it, about 15 per cent abort. Not every cow that has it aborts, but there is that risk of spreading it. If they carry the disease, they can abort later. If you do have an abortion and see the foetus, you know they have aborted; but if they re-absorb after they have been PD'd [pregnancy diagnosed] in calf and you haven't seen anything, you dry them off and they never calve. People always say they pick the dog muck up then leave it in a bag and pick it up later, which rarely happens.

I am quite positive about my future in farming, but there is a lot of negativity about dairy farming in the press and on social media. It's worrying that a video that doesn't even tell the truth about the industry can be shared and viewed thousands of times in a matter of days! However, there is always going to be a demand for food. •

Matthew Slack

Five years ago, we put in a new milking parlour. At the time, there were East Midlands Development Agency grants being offered, so we had a lot of grant funding for the milking parlour and cow health and welfare. We had a lot of mattresses, tipping water troughs to help keep clean water for cows, and cow brushes to help keep them clean. We also had activity monitors which show high or low activity and show cows in bulling. They are linked to the parlour by computer. The pedometer puts the cow's number into the individual computer at each milking stall. It [the computer] feeds the cow, records its yield, checks the conductivity of the milk to show if there's any mastitis and shows activity. Since then, we have not increased the herd, but over the next few years, we want to expand up to 200 cows so that me and my brother can take a decent living out of the farm.

We have definitely seen the benefit of this investment. It's improved the yields. When I left school, the yields were about 6,000 litres per cow a year. We were milking fifty-six cows. Now we're getting 10,000 litres with 120 cows. Cases of mastitis have dropped from about 40 per cent to 11 per cent last year. The milking equipment is far better. The pulsation is electric and not vacuum-operated. It's a lot more consistent. The old milking parlour was forty years old. It had had its day completely. Also, the automatic dipping and flushing system disinfects each unit between the cows, so there is no cross-contamination at milking time, which has made a big difference. And we have a teat-preparation brush which cleans the cow's teats and disinfects them a lot more effectively than we did before. At the moment, we average 5.2 lactations before the cows leave the herd, and their average age then is seven and a half years. Things are pretty good. The replacement rate is about 22 per cent. We have a lot of time for the cows and always try to put them first.

The milk price has been really challenging over the last two to three years. Just after we put the parlour in, we had a real good eighteen months. The milk price got up to 35p per litre for us, then it crashed two years ago. We got down to 17p, which is unsustainable for us. We drew 17.4p twelve months ago. It was pretty challenging, especially because we had invested so heavily over the last five years. All the reseeding work as well; we spent 20,000 pounds alone on lime in the last five years. But you still see a huge benefit with reduced feed costs from better quality forage.

The weather is always a challenge, but it's out of our control. Brexit is going to be a challenge for the industry, but I think the outcome will be positive. The milk price can be really challenging, as the last eighteen months have been, but we have a lot of confidence in Arla[17] and our future as farmer–owners of Arla. ●

'We have a lot of time for the cows and always try to put them first.'

---

[17] Arla Foods is a global dairy company and co-operative owned by 11,200 dairy farmers, around 2,400 of whom are British.

Graham Turnock

Graham, from Dun Lea Farm, Onecote, describes how the whole of his family have always been part of the business, which includes contracting.

When Dad and Mum were farming, Mum used to do the calves and grade the eggs. When me and my brother left school, we joined the business. Now with the extra land and stock, we're farming nearly 950 acres, including rented land. There's me and my brother David, my two sons, Andrew and Carl. My wife Carol does the calves, some milking and most of the paperwork. Andrew's wife Caroline helps with the sheep; Carl's partner Georgina helps with milking and some contracting; and we have three part-time staff: Jason, Ron and Simon.

Some small farmers who want contractors are finding it difficult to get someone to do the work because tackle is getting too big and everyone wants it doing yesterday. We do long days, mowing about 150 acres on a big day, but mostly maybe seventy to eighty acres a day because they're small. Depends on the fields – everything has to be right to do 150 acres. Grants help. Hedge planting, wall building, restoration and a bit of payment to help farmers along. I like seeing the machinery working. Got to keep up with modern stuff. I also like to see the wild birds, butterflies and the bees. •

Carl Turnock

Carl is Graham's youngest son and is himself a father. He describes the business and his role in it – mainly on the contracting side.

We have dairy mostly. We've got some beef and a lot of sheep. I mainly stick to the dairy side and the contracting. Involved in most aspects, I suppose. In the summer, we're doing contracting. Getting more and more in the winter as well – muck spreading, umbilical spreading mainly. That's the busiest thing at the moment in wintertime. In the summer, we're grass seeding, fertiliser spreading, baling, silaging, muck spreading as well. Apart from getting your machinery ready in a morning – greasing it up and doing any maintenance – your day can start as soon as the dew's off at eight, nine or ten o'clock. Then you can go right through, 'til nearly all night. We recently finished one at 4 a.m. Milking is my favourite job with animals, especially in winter. It's the warmest place. As regards contracting, it's mowing. That's a nice job.

We've got two sets of double mowers. Seem to crack on. You can do 140 acres in a day with one tractor and two mowers. In your gang, you've got your chopper, your mower, rake man, buck raking, three trailers or more – up to seven, depends how far you're going. Most we've had was thirteen men. These were other farmers. Subbies, I suppose you could call 'em. We've got four of us own. You need the trailers or the chopper man is waiting and that's dead money.

Carl Turnock on a tea break. **Photo**: Sheila Hine.

'It's the family farms … that might get through the tough times.'

Carl Turnock making haylage. **Photo**: Sheila Hine.

Fuel and wages are always going up. You can pass so much on, but there's tight margins in farming and contracting. There is quite a lot of competition round here. Ninety-nine per cent of people who we do work for are on Tesco contracts for their milk, which always helps. We've got a couple of bad payers. You sort of know who you can go to.

This year [2017] has been the worst – weather, more pressure, trying to get more done in a day. I suppose as a whole industry, everyone's in a rush nowadays, people won't wait. The loyalty is not with the job with there being so many other people doing it in the area. It's a case of 'I want to mow today; if you can't come, I'll ring somebody else.' And when you've invested money in the machinery, it's hard to not jump because you need the income, so it puts a lot of pressure on and that's where you get your long days.

I like the way of life with contracting because it gets you off the farm and it gets you meeting people you wouldn't have met before. You see a lot of different ideas on farms when you go around, good and bad. It's not very family-friendly, the long hours, and also in coming years when Dad retires, it would be a lot harder because he does a lot on the farm while we're away. It would mean employing someone else to do one or the other. Sometimes with paid labour, the attention to details is not always there. Also, the thing that gets me frustrated is that other professions such as plumbers or electricians, not necessarily more highly skilled than a farmer, when they go out on their job with their bare hands and a van and some tools, they charge in excess of 30 pounds an hour. Yet in farming, on the contracting side of things, you can go out with a tractor and trailer, a man driving and diesel and you're charging the farmer 30 pounds an hour and you've got hundreds of thousands of pounds invested in machinery, diesel, tyres and general maintenance.

The average price of a big tractor used for contracting work now is 100,000 pounds. A self-propelled chopper ranges from 150,000 to 250,000 pounds, mower-conditioner 15,000 to 18,000 pounds. A simple machine to row grass up: 20,000 pounds. We had a price on a four-rotor rake which can put fifty foot into one row. They're now 44,500 pounds, for a grass rake. A round baler and wrapper, which we've got; a combination baler wrapper is about 51,000 pounds. Big square balers: crazy money up to 80,000 to 100,000 pounds with a chopper and everything. Square bale wrapper would be another 27,000 pounds on top. Diesel is 50p a litre at the moment. Set of tyres for a very good brand: 5,000 pounds for four tyres. And mechanics charge you a nice sum of about 60 pounds an hour.

I feel more pressure now I have a son, and also there's the opposite side where you want to have something for him as well. So it spurs you both ways. You want something for him and you want to spend time with him, if that makes sense.

There's a lot of uncertainty at the minute with Brexit. No one knows where it's going to end. We seem to find it harder to get workers. Around here, a lot of people are struggling to get decent workers. There are not the younger people coming into it. I suppose the long hours and the pay isn't as good as other jobs.

I think being on a good milk contract always helps. That provides a more certain future as far as we can see at the moment. But also, with the supermarkets having a lot of power, you never know where it's going to go. There's a lot more automation coming into the industry, which helps on the labour side of things. Good or bad, I'm not sure. We've been looking into how a computerised system can be looking over your cows, twenty-four hours a day, seven days a week. They also have a rumination monitor which monitors the cow cudding, on a collar or ear tag. The earlier ones had a microphone which listened to the cow cudding, but the newer ones do it differently. They sense it.

The papers and people lead us to believe that getting bigger is the answer, but when times are hard, it's the family farms that don't have to pay big wages and don't have a lot of workers that might get through the tough times.

If you want to be a farmer, you have to do the paperwork. I wouldn't say I'm looking forward to that, but I am looking forward to my future in farming. ●

Andrew Turnock. **Photo**: Sheila Hine.

Andrew Turnock

Carl's brother Andrew works more with the animals in the substantial and very modern farm.

I do all sorts, really. On a typical winter morning, I scrape some of the milk cows out and move them round for milking. Then I clean the dry cows out and have a quick check round to see if any need putting out in the calving pens. Over half of the young stock are on bedding, which is done by hand and some with a wheelbarrow. I then give them corn and haylage. Then I feed the young stock (which are in cubicles) clamp silage with the feeder wagon. I feed just before breakfast and then again at night. In summer, there's a lot less bedding and feeding, so when we are off silaging I will probably spend at least two hours or so getting everything ready, checking over, greased up and fuelled up, hopefully spotting any little problem before it becomes a big one.

Depending on who's helping me, I start around about half past five, quarter past on a good day. When my cousin Jason's here, he does some jobs so I don't have start as early if I've had some late nights. If I started at quarter past five, we're mostly done for quarter past nine for breakfast. Then when all the jobs are done, we go out after breakfast and we can get on with something else.

I don't do as much contracting as Carl. He does a lot of the muck spreading and baling. I mainly drive the chopper, do odd bits of ploughing and things like that. I do enjoy driving the chopper. I don't really like anyone else to drive her. It's long hours, but I don't mind it. I do get a bit of headache for it, getting back late at night. It's made a difference now that I've got a wife and child. That's where I get the headaches from. I just have to try and not be too late, but then it's trying to keep everyone else happy. I did go away this summer on holiday for a week; that was nice to see my daughter for a bit. I wouldn't mind being a hands-on dad. I have changed a few nappies!

My wife's more into sheep than cows. It's what she's been used to at home, sheep. She'll be busy looking after two children soon. Hopefully she'll get more into cows and help a bit more with those eventually. How long you work depends what you're doing. When you're lambing, that's stupid hours, and same at silaging. I get quite a few midnight finishes. It seems to catch up with you more this time of year [November]. In the summer, it's not too bad. When the sun's out, you feel better. It does catch up with you at times, but I enjoy doing it and I think that helps.

I would probably cut back on the contracting before anything else, though I do enjoy doing it. Gets you away a bit – you see other people and how they do things and it's been good. You always think the grass is greener on the other side, but when you get there, it's just the same. You think, 'That field's good, better than ours.' But when you've been in it, it's no different, really.

'It's related to your PC or an app on your phone telling you whether a cow's poorly or needs inseminating.'

We've got CBs [radios] in the tractors, so you do hear a fair bit of mainly rubbish being spoken throughout the day. Part of a team, aren't you? There's banter. You used to have all your neighbours come and help you hay-make, but that day's gone. There is some good lads that come and help us out. You're always learning something. I quite enjoy being part of a team. I like being out in the field or the yard. I like feeding cows.

There's a lot of uncertainty at the minute. We're on a milk contract. That eases the pressure unless they change things. With the sheep, you haven't got that, so there's uncertainty. With Brexit coming, the sheep job looks uncertain. That's one good thing about contracting alongside farming. If sheep didn't do so well, there's always that.

In ten years' time, I'd like to be milking a few more cows. What we do with the sheep as a consequence of that, I don't know. I'd like to push cows a bit more and try and improve things, keep trying to improve the ground a bit. We've got a new seeder this time to try and get better grass in the pastures.

Environmental farming? It's probably good as a whole, but it's not something I'm really into. I'd sooner be improving things: doing some reseeding, draining and fencing. Probably when you get older, you slow down a bit and get more interested in birds and things, but it's not something I'm into at the moment. For some farmers, it does bring another income in, I suppose. It's for the good of everything in the countryside.

The other day, we had a rep come about a heat detection system for the cows, and he was saying it's a good system and everything, but in the future he was wondering about what it would be like for youngsters. They wouldn't have their own animal-husbandry skills with things relying on this system to pick up cows in heat or poorly. It's all related to your PC in the house or an app on your phone telling you whether a cow's poorly or needs inseminating. So that's what it might be like for mine and Carl's children if we don't keep pushing some of the old-fashioned ways. ●

Rob Belfield

Rob and Ruth Belfield, with their son James and daughter Sally, are hoping to future-proof Hurdlow Farm with pigs.

I had kept pigs when I was a teenager, so I knew a bit about them. I rang the area manager for a company who supply Waitrose, and he says, 'We're looking at a new generation of people to fatten our pigs. We have 40,000 sows all on an outdoor system with a five-year contract.' We looked at all the figures; we borrowed money again. We put the remaining wagon and shavings money in and built two 140-foot sheds to house 1,500 pigs. They come in at four weeks old, little tiny piglets. All we have to do is fatten them. The company own the pigs, and they give us the corn and the vets. We provide the straw and time and labour. They are gone in about twenty weeks. We have a wash out, have a break for a week, and start again. It's just fantastic. We can do everything we need to do in about an hour and half, and I think it is going to be the saviour of the farm.

'From a welfare point of view, this company are the Rolls-Royce of pig fattening.'

Rob Belfield

From a welfare point of view, this company are the Rolls-Royce of pig fattening. You clean out your sheds so there is no build up of disease, and they've got five vets working for them that come regular. Red Tractor come every two months inspecting. There's no big build up of slurry. We are hoping in the long term that what we spend on straw we can offset by cutting down on fertiliser. We can spread pig muck and it should all be to the benefit of the environment. We can't see a downside; they smell a bit, but no one lives there anyway. They're easy to work with. There is no calving them, no lambing them, sitting up at night, no TB issues. We just give them a pneumonia vaccine when they arrive and they are lovely animals to work with. James and Sally can look after them. It's fitting in really well. There is a lot less stress and I just thought if Brexit goes the wrong way and we lose the subsidies that we rely on, a regular income from a private company is guaranteed for five years. ●

'They are lovely animals to work with.'

Pigs on the Belfields' farm. **Photo**: Sheila Hine.

Sally Belfield

Sally lives with her parents and her brother on Hurdlow Farm. Her life, from a very young age, has revolved around farming and farm animals. She works full-time for the estate agent and agricultural surveyor Graham Watkins & Co in Leek. At just twenty-three, she has worked there for eight years, and spends evening and weekends helping out at home on the farm.

I've always been agriculturally minded. Farmers do seem to get on with me better because I know what I'm talking about with machinery and livestock. At the market generally I can do anything. I started when I was fourteen. I've done everything from sheep to poultry sales. I started droving sheep; then worked at poultry sales, clerking, booking in outside; then I got into the office more. I do the paperwork, the movement licences. I'm in charge of the pig movements. I make sure they all go through properly and are all correct. I check them off. Any problems farmers have with movements – ear tags, holding numbers, changes of cattle ear tags or details if some have got the wrong passport – I deal with those.

I support Graham and Rob Watkins in their valuations. I do a lot of the background work like finding comparables, doing plans, working out the area of farms. I do work for planning applications like agricultural justifications for conversions of barns or sheds. I help a lot with farm

James and Sally Belfield. **Photo:** Sheila Hine.

'I know what I'm talking about with machinery and livestock.'

dispersal sales and machinery sales – background work like meeting clients, getting to know them and what they want, what they want to sell and how it's all going to work.

I've always been a fan of livestock markets, always gone with my dad to Leek, Newark, Market Drayton and Bakewell. It's always been a big interest to me. I do love my job down there. I have a really good understanding of what goes on, like all your ear tags. I'm always giving people advice on what to do with their sheep. I know what tags they need and what movements they need. It's a big help with the Red Market, which enables farmers who are shut down with a TB breakdown to sell cattle for slaughter. They all have to have this TB24 licence, and a lot of farmers don't understand what those are. They don't know what to do to be able to sell stock, so I can give advice, which is a good help.

I've grown up with changing procedures like Electronic ID. We have to make sure that everything is electronically tagged now on the sheep side. Ear tags are a big issue now, so say someone comes along to a store lamb sale and purchases 400 lambs. They might only have 398 ear tags, and you've got to go round again and make sure you find which ones are missing. It's just to make sure everything is spot on.

These EID tags in general are very good for tracing animals, especially in the market. Down at Leek Market, with all the hurdles and gates for the big sheep sales, over 10,000 can be presented. It's a good setup when it works, but at night, it can be pitch-black darkness outside with the pens of lambs and you've got a lamb jumped into another pen. You know what tag you've got missing, you can go and scan that lamb and it belongs to that person and you can pull it out.

Waterhouses Young Farmers' Club is a big part of my life. I've been there since I was twelve. I joined in 2007. I was chairman last year, which I really enjoyed. I was treasurer for four years, winning best treasurer in the county twice, which is a big achievement for me. I've also done a lot of stock judging and public speaking competitions. The network of the Young Farmers movement is amazing. It can help you get into farming, and it's not just farming. I got the opportunity from Staffordshire Young Farmers to go to the Oxford Farming Conference for two days held in the Oxford University.

I would like to go into sheep farming. I love my sheep. We are all very commercially based here. We are moving into Aberfields Innovis breeding. It seems to be working well. But I do love Cheviots and Swales. I'm a big fan. I've always had Cheviot sheep myself or crosses. We bought some this time and put Aberfield on them to get strong mules, then stronger lambs again from those. It's just like a hobby on the side. I've always liked lambing. The problem is, I'm always working. I miss helping in a morning. I work Saturdays, so I'm only free on a Sunday, when I'm always doing pigs and stuff. In time, I'd like to cut down on work and help more at home.

I feel the future of farming could be quite prosperous. There are young people coming in. I do understand I've had it lucky where I am with Mum and Dad and my brother, just us four. It's grand, but a lot of people I know struggle because there's that many family members involved, or they want to rent a farm but there's that many running costs it's not worthwhile. There's more technical developments like these composite sheep and cattle breeds which seem to be paying off. I think it will go more that way.

Sat where I am now, I feel very lucky, but know a lot of people are in more difficult situations. It's sad to say, but it's hard work to get a step on the ladder. ●

Emma Trueman

Emma bought Roundhill Farm high up on Morridge, near Flash, in 2010. With the help of her brother, she farms forty-five acres at 1,500 feet at Morridge and another forty-five acres at Thorncliffe. She also has two jobs in Leek.

At the moment, it's just land and buildings. A house is work in progress. It's not like lowland as in Leek; it's completely different. Yesterday there was two to three inches of snow in the morning, and then it continued with snow and wind. I come up twice a day, morning and night; and then if something's for calving, I probably come more than that for a few hours. I work at the local vet and also at the cattle market, Leek Auctions. I just keep goin'. I just enjoy it, I enjoy being up here. I enjoy being out.

I've got thirty Beef Shorthorns. I try to breed heifers and bulls for the commercial men. One of the cows that I have got, one of her sons went to Stirling last month in the bull sale and topped the market at the Shorthorn sale at 12,000 guineas. Somebody bought him off me as an embryo calf and he took him up. But it's good for the cow and my breeding. I've shown for quite a few years. Last year, we ventured a bit further out, went to the Three Counties, Great Yorkshire, then the local shows. Yeah, I've done well showing, very well. Got one cow, last year she won some interbreed championships against other breeds. The first cow I took to Great Yorkshire, she was first in a class of fourteen.

Emma Trueman and David Watkins with her homebred bull Roundhill Lenny after being successfully shown at the Great Yorkshire Show. **Photo:** Sheila Hine

Now I'm into a native hardier breed. Before, I used to have some continental Limmy, pedigree Belgian Blues, and it was no good up here for them at all, whereas these are a lot hardier.

We've seen some grouse, in the rushes. And there's a pond where we used to get some waders in March or April time. We came out of environmental stewardship – it wasn't working. At the time, we had about 100 ewes and it was weather like this with snow and wind, and I gave them some hay in the field and they penalised me for it. So that was that. I would definitely consider it in the future. I'd try to increase the wild flowers because I like to see them. We have one field that we used to make hay in, but we haven't made hay here for five years because the weather's just not working with us. There's still some wild flowers in the back field. We tried some trees, but they don't grow. We've started rebuilding stone walls so hopefully we'll continue to do some every year. My brother Andrew helps when he can because he works full-time as well. He's a real help. I'm quite lucky, really – the cattle are pretty quiet, you can work with them. My brother helps clean out, put silage in and general things.

I would like to build a house up here one day when I've adjusted to the weather. When I bought it, it was somewhere to get me started, then hopefully I could buy something a little bit bigger, but I don't know if that will happen. It's a tough world. I've been lucky. Not many people would want to come and farm up here, so I think that gave me a bit of an advantage as it was cheaper. I just thought it was better to buy somewhere than plough all your money into renting, and at the end of the day you haven't that security to know you've got it from one year to the next.

We had it bad a few years ago. The snow was as high as the gates. We managed to park in a layby and walk, which isn't ideal, but we got here. We also shut the doors. If there's enough stock in, it will keep the water free and not freeze; and if we have to, there is a caravan where we could stay the night, just about. We're lucky we've not had to use it yet. In the summer, you can see down to Liverpool Docks from the top, but you still need your jumper – there's always a breeze. ●

'You can see down to Liverpool Docks from the top.'

The energy, expertise and determination of these young farmers is inspirational. No one could doubt their commitment to the future of farming in the South West Peak. But the conflicting ideas over what land is for that are expressed in this book will continue to be at the heart of discussions and policymaking on land use in this area and across Britain.

Seventy per cent of Britain is farmed land, but only three per cent is farmed organically. Andrew Sebire is one of the very few organic farmers in the South West Peak.

Andrew Sebire. **Photo**: Christine Gregory.

Andrew Sebire

Andrew Sebire and his wife Lesley took on a small dairy farm near Alderwasley in the 1970s before buying Lower Hurst Farm in the early 1980s, keeping beef cattle and some sheep. In 1988, they decided to specialise in building a pedigree herd of Hereford cattle. They have farmed organically for twenty years, and now run an organic meat-processing business.

We produce pedigree breeding cattle run on a mainly grass-fed suckler cow system. We think that the Hereford is a great all-rounder, a great general-purpose beef breed that has a lot to offer our home market. It's not a fussy or demanding grazer. It's prepared to take a rougher type of grassland and it can thrive perfectly well without concentrated feedstuffs to fatten it. And of course it's got this great reputation for succulent beef with marbling of the flesh. We calve about sixty, and then we keep calves with the cow until they're eight or nine months old. They don't rely on her at the end, but they do grow up together and then we wean the calves off. We feed turnips and clovers in the autumn. We don't buy any female cattle in, but new bull comes in every other year. We have to keep changing the bloodline.

In the mid-1990s, we started to get interested in the farm being run on an organic basis. It was the early days of interest in organics and it appealed to us. We went organic officially in 1998, and we have been very focused on that ever since. People talk about the fancy prices of organic food.

We've never been paid much extra for our organic beef, but we think it's the right way to farm. We think it's the future of farming, and that relying on chemicals and other artificial means of production is not going to last. So we're now researching, along with everybody else, how we go forward, and a great deal of that will depend on the government of the time.

The mood here and nationally is to go with more nature-friendly farming because we are concerned at long last about what's happening to our wildlife and our environment generally.

We always had lapwing, curlew and snipe here because we've got quite a lot of wet grassland on the farm. We're getting better and better all the time at using it. We've got a very good young farm manager with a very strong organic background and he's teaching us things we didn't know about. We control our grazing through electric fencing. He gets up at five o'clock in the morning, and when we go down after breakfast, the whole farm's different. The cattle have moved from one field to another and pastures are set up for them using electric wire. The parkland at the bottom was very inefficiently grazed in the old days. Now, through this system, we can break up grassland into smaller paddocks. They get used to it. They just think, 'When's the fence going to be moved?' They're mucking the area, grazing and treading it in so you get the reseeds from the plants themselves.

The biggest part of our business has now turned into the food production unit. After one of the big food scares – I think it was horse meat – Derbyshire County Council came to us out of the blue. They were interested in providing organic beef cuts and all the assurances that go with that, for school lunches throughout the county. This was a massive number of schoolchildren and we realised we couldn't supply this, so we have to buy in from other organic suppliers. It is all traceable. Now sometimes we supply eight or nine counties throughout the UK and we're always trying to get into new markets. We process everything here. We bring our own slaughtered carcasses back here and we also buy in forequarter from other organic producers. As we grow that business, the proportion of home-grown to bought goes down, but the ethos and assurance remains throughout.

'We could be paid to look after this landscape and to maintain it for future generations.'

It's a commercial success and makes up for the fact that we have a job making the farm side break even, and that's with farm subsidy coming in as well. We've been in Higher Level Stewardship for ten years and because we have all these interesting birds here we also have all sorts of other projects with our HLS. That scheme ends this year [2018], and we don't want to lose any of our management systems or our status. Under the current Countryside Stewardship, there is a Higher Level, but our advisers us tell us that it is very hard to achieve and means almost that you've got to become a conservation farm and nothing else. So we're beginning to do our homework on which of these options we can qualify for and benefit from.

We assume that whatever happens to Brexit, Mr Gove's Agriculture Bill will get through and that will open up all sorts of possibilities. They look like being interesting to ourselves and to many more farms. We could be guardians of the landscape. We could be paid to look after this landscape and to maintain it for future generations, accepting 'public money for public goods'.

I fear for the small farm. In terms of the value of what it can produce, it's going to be hard pushed to even make a living for the person who owns or tenants it. The only way is for small farms to be recognised as a vital part of the existing landscape and habitat for wildlife which we wish to preserve. And for farmers to be paid as (you can call it) park keepers.

Paid to resist as people come along and say, 'We'd love to have your place – will you sell it?' The obligation which would go with the property is that it must only be a farm.

The answer lies in forgetting trying to make these smaller farms profitable, but to call them 'public goods'. Public good gives every small farm a chance. It's all about money in the end. The money would only be there, provided that they stay there and look after the land. If people are paid a kind of salary to be there on small farms and are content to look after them, they don't have to work out how to make a living wage from the farm. What can you do if you're not able to make a living out of your small farm? You don't call it charity; you say, 'I'm simply providing a public good. I'm here to look after something and hand it on to future generations, something which our ancestors will be forever proud of: that I had a worthy job in life, which is to keep that place going and to provide part of the landscape.' ●

Farming is at the heart of the history and culture of the hills and valleys of the South West Peak, but food production in the uplands is unlikely to be the top priority for this and future governments. We end with thoughts from Bill Brocklehurst and Helen Heathcote, who are now retired from farming, but who share a conviction that a greater connection to the natural world is vital to the future of both farming and wildlife.

Brown hare in rough grazing; a species that can indicate the level of biodiversity in a farmed landscape. **Photo**: Christine Gregory.

Bill Brocklehurst

There's got to be a shilling in it for everybody, for t' farmer, for t' birds. There were plenty of subsidies, but now they've paid farmers to clear sheep off hills. What a waste of money. Why didn't they cut the numbers of sheep down to an acceptable level? They've got for t' get stock back on the hills in reasonable numbers, but this here open-ended giving farmers and landowners a bucket of money every year just for not keeping things on t' hills, it's gonna dry up one day, that is. Put some sheep back on t' hills, cattle in some places where it's acceptable, and do away with four-wheeler motorbikes. Make the people shepherd the animals, not whizz round on a motorbike, scaring everything. That's not sheep farming. Instead of paying farmers a big bag of money for t' not, pay him a lesser amount of money for t' pay towards a man's wage for going shepherding them sheep. And make 'em do it, not draw money and never go near 'em.

They've got all these training establishments. Surely they can knock a bit of sense in a teenager's head, for t' put one foot in front of t' other and look at sheep and know them. Somebody can go into a college or run a nice big class. Teach 'em – it'll get rid of the obesity. It'll learn 'em how for t' use a dog. While he's doing that, he'll know how many curlews are on t' moor, how many plovers; or if he sees a ring ouzel, give him another ten pound a week or something for keeping his eyes open. But they've got to have feet on the ground. •

Helen Heathcote

The reason I haven't got any cows now, I have arthritis in my hands. I had Aberdeen Angus, big cows. I ended up with Dexters because they are smaller. Worst part was the animals going. When the cattle wagons go and you get up the next day and they are gone, it's deathly. When mine went, it's like it was with Dad – he was killing himself. He was sixty-four, he had a bad hip and his brother had an ulcer. My son was too young to take it on, and my brother was off high-flying. The farm just went. It's a shame to think we are a big family, an extended family, and there is nobody farming at all. It's a way of life, isn't it? It's a vocation. Nowadays, when you talk to young ones, all they are interested in is where they will get, what to do with their money or where they are going at weekend. They're not really interested.

Farmers have all got other jobs, or they are getting older and people are just dying out and farmers can't afford to buy the farms, can they? Latterly, the outlying farms were being bought by business people playing at farms. They commute in to Birmingham and Manchester. But it's kept its roots round here. In time, it will go the way of everywhere else.

I used to call the cows my stress busters. I used to go in the barn when they were cudding. They just lay there, sounds eccentric. They kind of talked to you. It takes the weight of the world away. You miss the animals. I miss them now. Three years ago, I had my own really nice herd of Dexters. I had my own bull. I used to do everything by hand. I was a barrow and fork person. People do not do barrows and forks any more. They get the tractor out, belching fumes. I don't think you can pollute all the time. You need to be kind. No one is kind any more. Nobody thinks about anyone any more – it's all 'I'm alright, Jack', isn't it?

This morning, when I walked the dog, I stopped because I saw the skylarks. I thought, the sound of lapwings and curlews, how many people hear that? ●

'I don't think you can pollute all the time. You need to be kind.'

Friesian heifers, autumn dawn. **Photo**: Sheila Hine.

ACKNOWLEDGEMENTS

This book and its associated oral history archive are the products of several years of discussion, planning and hard work. Since 2014, many people have contributed generously with their time, ideas and expertise. Karen Shelley-Jones, as the Scheme Manager for the South West Peak Landscape Partnership hosted by the Peak District National Park Authority, first gave the green light to this venture and has held the project together from the outset with her unwavering support, organisational input, ideas, information, contacts, maps and documents, and by keeping us on track.

We are grateful to the National Lottery Heritage Fund who have generously provided the funding for this project and made it possible. Thanks to Mary McNaught, formerly from the Farming Life Centre, who has been at the heart of the project from the start as an enthusiastic administrator, chief communicator and business manager. She has also spent hundreds of hours transcribing interviews, contacting farmers and contributing ideas and maintaining contacts. We must also thank Catherine Stuart-Jervis, Keith Bradshaw and Rachel Metcalfe from the Farming Life Centre for their invaluable roles in managing and maintaining the business side of the project. Julia Cook as former Farming Life Centre manager, as a member of the farming community of the South West Peak, and as a friend has been an invaluable source of information, contacts and ideas. It was her initial proposal that provided the basis of the project. We thank Mike Shurmer, Senior Conservation Officer for the Midlands Region of the RSPB, for his input on waders. Both Patricia Stubbs and Isabella Stone (from the Campaign to Protect Rural England) have read various drafts and provided much valued comment, feedback, moral support and friendship. We are especially grateful to Colin Tudge for his insightful and comprehensive foreword. Thanks to Jon Barton and the team at Vertebrate for their guidance, editorial advice and expertise in transforming our words and images into this book, especially to Emma Lockley, who was a patient and careful midwife to the last stages of the book's production. Also a big thank you to Nathan Ryder for his wonderful design work that has made this book a delight to look at.

Last and most importantly, a huge thank you to all those farmers we interviewed and their families who were generous with their time, made us welcome in their homes and trusted us with their thoughts and memories.

OVERLEAF: Male Wheatear – a summer visitor to the South West Peak. **Photo**: Christine Gregory.